# Farm Animal Behaviour

The illustration on the cover is taken from a mediaeval manuscript of c. 1200 and shows the exchange of nursing stimuli between a cow and its calf.

# FARM ANIMAL BEHAVIOUR

An introductory textbook on the study of behaviour
as applied to horses, cattle, sheep and pigs

ANDREW F. FRASER
MRCVS, MVSc (Toronto), FIBiol
Senior Lecturer, Department of Veterinary Surgery and Obstetrics
Royal (Dick) School of Veterinary Studies
University of Edinburgh

The Williams & Wilkins Company
Baltimore

SANS
TACHE

Baillière Tindall
7 & 8 Henrietta Street, London WC2E 8QE

Cassell & Collier Macmillan Publishers Ltd, London
35 Red Lion Square, London WC1R 4SG
Sydney, Auckland, Toronto, Johannesburg

The Macmillan Publishing Company Inc.
New York

*First published 1974*

ISBN 0 7020 0445 6

Published in the United States of America by
The Williams and Wilkins Company, Baltimore

Printed in Great Britain by Cox & Wyman Ltd,
London, Fakenham and Reading

# Preface

CERTAIN major books on the behaviour of domesticated animals have emerged in recent years and have become established as comprehensive and definitive reference works. These books and their successive editions are unlikely to lose their authority, but, somewhat paradoxically, through their existence and status they have created a further need for literature of a more introductory nature. This textbook has been written to meet that need and to serve as an introduction to the subject of applied behaviour studies in farm animals.

The book has been written for students taking agricultural, veterinary and animal science courses, in particular, but it is also intended that the book should be useful to graduates in various scientific disciplines who require convenient access to general knowledge on the behaviour of farm animals. Others who are concerned with the behaviour and welfare of these animals may also find the book informative.

In the text an explanatory and descriptive approach to the scientific study of behaviour has been taken. Technical terms are unavoidable, and indeed valuable, in presenting a scientific subject but an attempt has been made to limit their use. A glossary of such terms has been provided at the end of the book for reference purposes, but it will serve also as introductory material to the objective science of behaviour, or ethology, and the reader's early attention to this section is therefore invited.

Descriptions of animal behaviour need the support of authentic illustrative material and throughout the book fairly liberal use has been made of line drawings. Many of these have been appended 'tracing' or 'drawing' denoting the illustration to be a tracing of a photograph, or an artist's drawing. At the end of each chapter selected reference material is listed which points the way to deeper and more extensive information relevant to the chapter.

No reference in the text has been made to the *Proceedings of the Society for Veterinary Ethology*, but special mention of this literature must be made. The author has been a co-editor of the *Proceedings* from their commencement in 1966 till the present time and has therefore been in a very privileged position to draw information from them. This has been done freely and fully. It could be even stated that this textbook has emerged, to a large extent, from the *Proceedings*. In making this declaration, acknowledgement must be made to the original suggestion from members of the Society for Veterinary Ethology that this should be done by the author when sufficient material had been accumulated. Most of the *Proceedings* have been published bi-annually in the *British Veterinary Journal* and these, together with the fuller papers heard at a score of scientific symposia organized by the society have provided much of the raw material from which this book has been constructed.

In the past the economic basis under which agriculture was of necessity carried out may have rendered any satisfactory behavioural studies of domesticated farm animals impractical, but the needs of production and the resultant intensification of husbandry have made it imperative that man should have more knowledge and a better understanding of exactly what he is doing with the animals under his control, and on which he is dependent for sustenance.

Much of the impetus which has encouraged further developments and projected studies in farm animal behaviour in Britain has been provided by the Brambell Report which is discussed in the first chapter of this book.

The Report drew attention to the question of the welfare of domesticated animals under conditions of intensive husbandry. The Society for Veterinary Ethology, which was subsequently formed, has concerned itself with ethological developments founded on the belief that veterinary ethology constitutes practical applied ethology. A constructive and important reason for furthering the establishment of ethology as an applied science and a branch of biology in its own right is that ethological research may have advantageous bearings on the farm animal industry and its methods of production.

Many hold the view that the study of ethology is at a very early stage, and that with greater financial resources and scientific effort considerable development will be made. The key to further development may lie in the pursuit of studies of an experimental nature which will encourage the interest of those working in other

## Preface

disciplines. Apart from work of an experimental nature it is apparent that more observational studies would be beneficial to the advancement of the welfare of domestic animals. Welfare studies can make a definite contribution and be beneficial to the farm animal industry generally. Some of the methods of intensive husbandry and productivity which many find unacceptable on humanitarian grounds may also be economically detrimental in the long term.

It is encouraging to find that more work is now being initiated on farm animal welfare. Projects of particular interest are in progress on environmental factors and the incidence of disease. Other studies include the effect of group size, density and physical environment on behaviour. Research being carried out currently suggests that, when more is known about the effects of different systems of husbandry on the performance and behaviour of farm animals, livestock producers will be guided along very different lines to those presently being pursued.

Those who study the subject of applied animal ethology beyond the limits of this book can discover that it is an area of infinite depth. While it was the original intention to construct a bridge to ethology with this elementary textbook perhaps it would be more accurate to regard it as a springboard.

The author wishes to express his gratitude to the many associates who helped in the preparation of this book. In particular the assistance of Mr R. B. Callicott in the production of the illustrations is gratefully acknowledged. The considerable assistance of Mr Neil Fraser and of the publishers, Baillière Tindall, in the evolution of the manuscript is also fully appreciated and acknowledged.

*September, 1973*                                    ANDREW F. FRASER

# Contents

# Part I
# FUNDAMENTALS

# 1.

# Principles of Ethology

ANIMAL behaviour is the overt and composite functioning of
animals individually and collectively. The study of animal behaviour, whilst by no means a new one, has only been pursued scientifically in recent decades. Many early observers, possibly as far
back as cavemen, found the activities of animals fascinating. To
this day observations on active animals have come to the attention
of those who are responsible for their maintenance as well as many
who are only distantly or casually involved. The fact remains,
however, that for these observations to have validity and for them
to be communicable, they have to conform to scientific principles.
This means that the observations should be capable of being noted
repeatedly by the same observer and others with appropriate
training. The observations should concern what is visible and
apparent and avoid a subjective appraisal of behaviour. As with
some other subjects there are circumstances when scientific principles cannot satisfy the demand for information and understanding.
Circumstances may create a sudden demand for information which
has not been built upon extensive study. When these circumstances concern animal welfare, it is regrettably necessary to
depart from scientific principles occasionally. This changeover
from the objective approach to the subjective, while occasionally
obligatory, should be avoided whenever possible by the student
of animal behaviour. It is necessary to maintain a conscious
attempt at objectivity in this field of study more than in many
other fields, so that the observer does not delude himself or others
and so that this subject can continue to develop as a branch of
biology and a science in its own right.

The study of animal behaviour has been pursued, in the course
of its development, in two main types of situation. On the one
hand, much work has been done on free-living animals and their
natural habitats; this work reveals the repertoire of habits of these
animals under natural conditions. On the other hand, a much
more experimental form of study has been pursued by workers

dealing with animals which have been set specific tasks; this is perhaps the area which is most immediately profitable to the research worker. For a time it was only the study of the behaviour of free-living animals which was classed as ethology.

Literally, the term ethology means the study of habits and customs; and veterinary ethology is applied to the customs and habits of animals. However, no definition stands still indefinitely and ethology, since it implies that scientific formalities are employed, is now widely used to describe all those earnest attempts at observing and detailing, in objective fashion, the behaviour of animals under all manner of circumstances, including domestication. It has been said that words have no meaning and that the meanings are in people. It must be recognized that the term ethology has now acquired a much broader definition than originally given for the increasing number of scientists who study it.

## THE ROLE OF ETHOLOGY

The study of animal physiological systems and the functions of the discreet anatomical items is undoubtedly of enormous help to the student of ethology. But those studying the workings of animal parts are the first to admit that this knowledge, however fulsome, does not provide a satisfactory understanding of the mechanism of the whole. Conversely, there are other biologists who, having studied animal behaviour, may speculate on the function of certain parts, such as the cerebrum. This approach is no more satisfactory than the first. Clearly, what is needed is a broad, basic understanding of physiology and anatomy together with numerous supporting disciplines, such as mathematics. Not least of all, a general knowledge of animal recognition is required if an ethologist is to be competent.

The acquisition of knowledge alone has justified scientific studies on a massive scale. Ethology, as a scientific discipline, can justifiably be studied for its own sake. Almost certainly the earlier students of the subject, and many current ones, had no other motive in selecting this subject as a major interest. Gradually, however, more pressures are being put on ethology students, both by animal husbandry scientists who wish to modify the ways in which animals are husbanded and by that section of the informed public, which has acquired some conscience about the manner in which animals are utilized by mankind.

Nowadays animal scientists must all have a working knowledge of animal behaviour. It is impossible though for any one person to acquire a satisfactory depth of knowledge about the behaviour of several species of animals. One therefore sees increasing numbers of students being forced to concentrate on a limited number of species. The species for main concern now are farm animals, namely horses, cattle, pigs, sheep, goats and poultry. The public concern over animal welfare is similarly largely directed at these species. The farm animal scientist is now expected to be able to provide scientific information about the behaviour of these species, as a result of sound instruction and personal observation. Modern farm animal scientists, whether they like it or not, are expected by the majority of people therefore to be competent to act as experts on matters concerning farm animal welfare. Indeed as the farm animal industries become more technologically minded, more stock-keepers are prepared to accept informed comment on animal behaviour and its relevance to animal welfare.

# ETHOLOGY AND ANIMAL WELFARE

In Britain the close relationship between animal husbandry, farm animal ethology and animal welfare was probably forged by the work of the Brambell Committee. This was a government technical committee set up in 1965 under the chairmanship of the late Professor Rogers Brambell, and included a small number of people with diverse interests in farm animal production. This committee's report is relevant to animal welfare in animal reproduction throughout the world. The Brambell Report placed emphasis on the lack of behavioural studies on the welfare of animals kept under intensive methods of husbandry. It stressed that these studies were important not only for the animals concerned but also for the welfare of the animal industry. The Report questioned the soundness of taking one single parameter of production such as growth rate, egg or meat production, as the only reliable measure of the suitability of a system of husbandry. It pointed out that any sufficient estimate of an animal's welfare must be based, not only on the physical evidence of productivity, but also on the behaviour of the animals thus maintained. Such behaviour should be viewed in the light of the known ethology of the particular species.

The Brambell Committee was bold in tackling the subject of anthropomorphism. In anthropomorphism the observer ascribes to animals, feelings and sensations that are essentially his own, or at least, those that are recognized as being human. The Brambell Report questions whether it is valid to assume that feelings of this nature are necessarily exclusively human. It is pointed out that there are sound physiological and anatomical reasons for accepting that domestic animals and birds experience the same kind of sensations as do human subjects. The structure of the sensory organs and the nervous systems of animals is basically similar to that in man. While sensations, for example the senses of hearing and smell, may differ in degree between man and the domesticated species, it is arguable that they are basically similar. It is equally justifiable to assume that they are in many ways similarly equipped to share in some of the feelings that we recognize as being characteristically human, even if in this latter category, we concede that the human being has a greater capacity for qualitative feeling. The Report stated that it could see no reason for conceding 'mind' to fellow man but not to animals. Mental functions, it was viewed, are of neurological origin in man and higher animals alike. Since the committee was principally concerned about animal welfare, it attempted to decide how the suffering of an animal can be evaluated. The committee acknowledged that it is impossible to measure suffering in people, and that we judge suffering in others by analogy with our own feelings. Animal suffering must similarly rest on analogy with human suffering and the evaluation must be derived from similar signs, viz. observation of voice, expression, reaction and general unusual demeanour which together amount to behaviour. The committee insisted that animals show unmistakable signs reflecting pain, exhaustion, fright, frustration, rage and other emotions; any one of which may indicate a degree of suffering. Further, it pointed out that experienced stockmen were able to detect unusual signs in their animals and to appreciate the implications of these with regard to suffering.

Suffering cannot be determined objectively and we must rely ultimately on a subjective judgment. Undoubtedly, this will always be so. The Brambell Report protested against arguments which implied that animal husbandry practices in operation cannot be interfered with on welfare grounds without scientific proof of suffering as unworthy, however plausible. Professor Brambell asked whether, if a child is thought to be suffering, action is taken on subjective judgment or on some scientific evidence. This is reminiscent of the statement by a leading biologist, a lady, who made the claim, a quarter of a century ago, that she could 'understand' the behaviour of animals as competently as the behaviour of her children. It is clear that the public's conscience over modern methods of animal husbandry, takes the form of increasing activity under the heading of animal welfare.

It is not inappropriate that animal welfare should concentrate on the domestic animals, since domestication of any kind necessarily involves some degrees of confinement and restraint. The forms of restraint that are applied depend on the methods of husbandry, and the species to which it is applied. In addition individual idiosyncrasies determine the depth of restraint to be applied. In the past, acceptable restraints have been practised by generations of stockmen. Modern stockmen are no less well meaning but modern intensive methods of animal productivity demand a greater control over the animals and their environment. This control includes limitations on space, diet, ventilation, illumination, bedding and companionship. As the Brambell Report pointed out: 'It is because of these various restraints imposed on the animal by the artificial environment of intensive husbandry that the whole question of welfare has become so crucial today.' The committee's report was summed up by the following statement: 'Above and beyond all these matters stands the fact that modern intensive animal production methods, most markedly increase the responsibility of those who use them towards the animals in their charge. If any creature is wholly and continuously under control, we believe that this total human responsibility must be acknowledged; changing patterns of husbandry may mean varying degrees of frustration and discomfort to animals whose normal patterns of behaviour are still imperfectly understood. We are certain that a beginning must be made to safeguard their welfare.'

Animal scientists have come to realize that there are many ways in which ethology can help with the welfare of animals and thereby ensure more profit from more sensible husbandry. For example, comparative studies on feral animals help to throw light on the behaviour patterns of domesticated species. Studies of this kind have been helpful in clarifying the importance, in the lives of modern farm animals, of such environmental factors as social companionship, regular feeding and resting regimes, and the rhythms of other activities such as sleeping and breeding. For ethology to continue to contribute substantially to profitable animal husbandry more and more exponents are required to fill the gaps in knowledge. Where can we better apply animal ethology than in those species which are totally under our control and totally dependent on us for sustenance and existence.

# OBJECTIVITY AND THE STUDY OF BEHAVIOUR

A paradoxical situation has developed while the study of animal behaviour has become a very exact science. Modern contributors to the subject have shown the need for exactitude and the correct ways of applying it. As a result this field of study has expanded dramatically and has taken a permanent place in the foremost ranks of the scientific disciplines. For some time now it has been well equipped with its own terminology, methods of research and rapidly expanding literature. At the same time, because of the increasing concern about utilizing animals under modern systems of husbandry, the moral factors involved have been passed on to the student of behaviour. He is, therefore, unable to maintain scientific aloofness, and in the application of ethology to the farm animals, he is forced to compromise between his scientific position and moral concern for the welfare of the subjects he studies. Perhaps for this reason, the applied ethologist will never be at one with what we might term the fundamental ethologist. The principal concern of the latter is not so much the animal, as the exactitude of the study of the animal's behaviour.

A major goal in the study of animal behaviour is objectivity, as has been stated already, nevertheless we must recognize that complete objectivity is never possible. At some stage in formulating an observation, the observer relies on his own impression of what the animal has done. If instruments are in use, he is utilizing an impression of what he reads on an instrument. Since, some element of subjectivity will inevitably be involved in studying animal behaviour, the student must aim at a sensible relationship between what is clearly evident on one hand and what is presumed on the other. Strained attempts to avoid subjectivity usually lead to deceptive results. Feigned objectivity is even less desirable than unwitting subjectivity.

The principal form of subjectivity in the study of animal behaviour is anthropomorphism; it is often involved in attempts at interpreting motivation. It is a first principle that the behaviour of an animal involves a great deal more than mechanical motion and that both internal and external factors are involved in the manifestation of behaviour. Some early students of behaviour adopted purist positions and considered that only externally observable factors should be recognized. The taboo on reported behaviour, which did not meet these standards, deterred a great many animal scientists from becoming involved in ethology for a long time. Fortunately the position is now changed and while anthropomorphic interpretation of behaviour is widely recognized as undesirable in ethology, its occasional use may be permissible. Today it is probably sufficient to recognize anthropomorphism to be a trap for the unwary, but that its limited use can help in gaining insight into the activities of animals. Indeed it is a fact that those, who are most experienced in dealing with living animals, are those who are most likely to utilize anthropomorphism effectively in understanding the animals in their charge. With this understanding, they are able to cope with them much more effectively than any pure scientist would be able to, if he lacked practical knowledge of that particular type of animal.

The student of ethology must realize that there are other undesirable methods of studying the subject; anecdotal reports of behaviour have now virtually no place in modern ethology. These accounts, since they are largely dependent on the memory and recall of the observer and subsequent reporting by word of mouth, have no scientific value. Narratives of what animals have been seen to do may be of interest but, unless these reports are put together in a scientifically acceptable way, they are of little help. Indeed, when such stories of behaviour circulate and find their way into animal lore, it takes a massive amount of subsequent scientific observation to delete them. Anecdotes concerning animal behaviour may be acceptable for teaching purposes when utilizing the story to illustrate a point but, even then, this will probably be only an indication that the teacher lacks material.

Two main approaches to the formal study of animal behaviour still persist; these are the psychological and the physiological approaches to ethology. Those ethologists with a physiological view of the subject are principally concerned with identifying, in behavioural terms, the functioning of the central and the peripheral nervous systems. Ethologists, with the psychological view of the subject, are in their turn principally interested in the phenomenon of behaviour itself; they view behaviour as one of the body's systems and study the behaviour of the animal with the environment as a back-drop. This involves a search for a link between environment and behaviour. The two schools can readily co-exist and indeed do so for the benefit of ethologists who wish to apply ethological principles under what can be termed practical conditions. Many ethologists take the compromise view that behaviour mediates between the physiological conditions, on the one hand, and the animal's immediate environment, on the other. Clearly although there are separate schools of thought they are not so far apart as to leave a central gap. Indeed the central area is the one most favoured by practical students of ethology.

## ROOTS OF BEHAVIOUR

The opening of this chapter describes behaviour as overt and complex activities. Quite clearly there are activities which are overt yet not very complex. Reflexes come into this category, but since they are seldom exhibited in isolation from any other bodily movement, reflex activities form an important part of the formal subject of physiology, and are important as ethological features. One particular type of reflex is the conditioned reflex. It is now recognized that this is a fundamental mechanism in learning at all levels.

Behaviour has its origins in many factors. Apart from conditioned reflexes and learning there is the role of instinct in animal behaviour to be considered. Again, the effect of the environment on the animal organism can be seen in its behaviour; and since this environment is made known to the animal through diverse sensory systems, these must also be studied. Some stimuli are perceived by the organism at close quarters, others at longer range. The motivation which the animal receives dictates behaviour, and some of this motivation, if not the bulk of it, derives from internal factors. Some of these factors are best appreciated as drives. The hypothesis with regard to drives underlying the behaviour of animals also requires study. Other forms of internal motivation are clearly based on physiological factors such as the content of the alimentary canal or the level of hormone production by the various endocrine glands. Here the endocrinology of the animal must be grasped for a satisfactory understanding of ethology. There are circumstances in which an animal has its behaviour dictated by factors which are in conflict with each other. This conflict is seen in the resultant behaviour as threat displays and displacement activities. The student should be aware that no single factor is responsible for the behaviour of an animal under most circumstances. Some animals and certain species, in particular, exhibit forms of behaviour which they have acquired genetically. This inherited behaviour plays quite a prominent role in the behaviour manifest by the farm animals. Since the finishing touches of learning add to the repertoire of an animal's inherent behaviour, it is important for the student to appreciate the ways in which learning processes normally take place in farm animals. If its learning is deficient an animal will remain deprived of some of the functions possessed by others of its kind and as a result it is likely to be a less adaptable organism than it should be.

A study of the sundry factors capable of affecting the behaviour of an animal must include the various early experiences which can permanently affect the behaviour of that individual into its adult life. Environmental factors and forces have a much more powerful and durable influence, when applied in early life, than similar ones experienced in adult life. The immature organism is clearly much more malleable and ductile, to borrow physical terms, than is the adult animal.

# EARLY EXPERIENCE AND BEHAVIOUR

Social and environmental experiences of an animal tend to have more effect the earlier in life they are experienced. The organism is seen to benefit from as great a variety of environmental stimulations as possible in early developmental life.

The effects of early experience on behaviour have to be seen under several categories.

*Critical periods.* These occur in the early post-neonatal life of the animal during which the administration of social and environmental stimulation has a marked and protracted effect on development and behaviour. These infantile periods are shortlived and if the experiences are not registered within the critical period, the opportunity for the animal to gain most from them is lost. The critical periods have also been termed 'sensitive periods'. Some of them coincide with the first operation of senses, such as sight, hearing and smell. *Imprinting* is one process of rapid learning which takes place early in the post-neonatal critical periods of an animal's life. This is the process whereby a neonate animal develops social preferences, usually towards its own species and in particular towards its own dam, and is generally found to be irreversible. It is continued into adult life where it determines features of behaviour such as the attitude of the animal towards humans and other members of its own kind. There are also long term effects upon sexual behaviour resulting in incomplete imprinting processes.

*Infantile experience.* This deals with environmental stimulation sometimes experienced by the animal between birth and weaning. During this period the total effects of learning are compounded. The development of emotions, the opportunity to pursue exploratory behaviour, the social experiences of the young animal and the development of its physical and physiological apparatus, all combine to influence the animal's subsequent behaviour.

*Post-weaning environmental experiences.* These play their part in developing the behaviour of the animal in later life. Learning processes can continue into this period and senses also continue to develop to improve the animal's awareness of its environment. Social experiences are still occurring at this age, and investigatory activities increase at this stage.

In these various ways it can now be seen that environmental factors have a very considerable impact upon the developing organism, and predetermine the nature of its behaviour as an

12

adult in a wide range of situations from feeding to its behaviour among groups of animals.

The behaviour of animals falls into various patterns, each pattern having its own function. The principal behavioural patterns are included in the following list: (1) ingestive behaviour; (2) eliminative behaviour; (3) care-seeking behaviour; (4) caregiving behaviour; (5) sexual behaviour; (6) agonistic behaviour; (7) allelomimetic behaviour; (8) investigatory behaviour; (9) shelter seeking; (10) dominance; (11) leadership; (12) territoriality; and (13) social relations. The principal behaviour systems in animals may differ from species to species; and some systems are better developed than others. Again some systems, since they are more important commercially than others, have been studied quite intensively while others have been neglected somewhat. While this lack of knowledge might impede the student's initial study of the subject, it nevertheless provides an opportunity for very rewarding research in this field.

# SUPPLEMENTARY READING

CARTHY, J. D. (1966) *The Study of Behaviour. The Institute of Biology's Studies in Biology No. 3.* London: Edward Arnold.

DETHIER, V. G., & STELLAR, E. (1961) *Animal Behaviour.* London: Prentice Hall.

HUME, C. W. (1956) *In Praise of Anthropomorphism.* London: Universities Federation for Animal Welfare.

CARTHY, J. D. & EBLING, F. T. (1964) *The Natural History of Aggression.* New York: Academic Press.

MANNING, A. (1967) *An Introduction to Animal Behaviour.* London: Edward Arnold.

MATTHEWS, L. H. (1964) Overt fighting in mammals. In: *Natural History of Aggression,* ed. J. D. Carthy & F. T. Ebling. New York: Academic Press.

MOLTZ, H. (1971) *The Ontogeny of Vertebrate Behavior.* New York and London: Academic Press.

SCOTT, J. P. (1958) *Animal Behavior. The Natural History Library.* New York: Anchor Books, Doubleday.

# 2.

# Theoretical Ethology

THE development of ethology as a science has been characterized by attempts to create valid concepts of a hypothetical nature regarding the causes of behaviour. These concepts have been successful in explaining the basis of behaviour and now constitute the basic theory of the subject. The central philosophy of modern ethology seems to be on a much more secure basis now than it was only a very few years ago. The prevailing ideas are those which have survived the very critical period during which ethologists of many nationalities were largely concerned with testing the validity of each other's theories.

When ethologists attempt to understand the causation of behaviour, they cannot make much progress, particularly when dealing with behaviour in its most complete and complex forms. The breaking-up of behaviour patterns into component units, which can logically be considered in isolation, is necessary in attempts to specify behaviour. The obvious interrelationships between these units encourage the postulation of the various concepts, which together become the theory of the subject. Such theory generates its own technical glossary and the extensive acceptance and use of this common vocabulary improves the exchange of technical ideas among students of the subject. The fact remains though that, however valid various hypotheses might be, it is important to realize that theoretical concepts are principally of use in the teaching of the subject. They are, therefore, a means to an end; the end being a comprehensive appreciation of the significance of behaviour.

## THE CONCEPT OF INSTINCT

Instinct is the principal concept in ethology which a newcomer to the science has to consider. The term has a popular meaning, but deeper study will show that its denotative meaning in ethology is rather different and requires fresh consideration.

Instinctive behaviour is that element of behaviour which has been inherited. This inherited instructive behaviour may be modified during the life of the animal, according to its experiences with its environment; but in the main, instinctive behaviour reveals itself as complex behaviour which embodies a variety of stereotyped units. This instinctive pattern provides adaptability. As a form of adaptation it is subject to change with natural selection; but at the individual level instinct ensures that the animal is equipped with a fairly elaborate repertoire of adaptive responses which can be utilized without prior experience.

The central nervous mechanism which determines instinct is already established in the brain of the young animal at the time of its birth or even at the prenatal stage. All that is required is for environmental factors to materialize and set in motion pre-set behaviour patterns which are aimed at ensuring quick and effective adaptation of the individual concerned.

Clearly, natural selection has provided the individual with a set of responses, which can be brought into play where any delay in acquiring appropriate responses through the trial and error processes of learning might prove fatal to the individual.

Instinctive behaviour has certain definitive features. These behaviour patterns are essentially inherited, specific and complex. Instinctive responses are firstly organized in the higher nervous centres, and are similarly organized in genetically similar animals. Instinctive patterns should thus be seen as identical patterns in all or the majority of animals of the same type. Secondly, instinctive responses from an animal are only typically elicited in that species in response to some specific stimulation. This is not only their identifying feature but their principal role. Thirdly, behaviour patterns of an instinctive nature are essentially complex, but in their complexity they are stereotyped with one small unit of behaviour blending into others.

There are other forms of stereotyped inborn behaviour, kinesis and taxis for example, but instinctive behaviour has further identifying features, viz:

1. Instinctive behaviour is released promptly by a key stimulus in the environment which once commenced, will proceed to the

terminal fraction of the pattern. The environment, therefore, does not guide the animal in its behaviour; it merely releases it.

2. Instinctive behaviour, if it does not find an outlet, tends to accumulate its energy so that it becomes, in time, more readily evoked by a minimum of stimulation.

Instinctive behaviour can be described as a complex hierarchially organized nervous mechanism which is susceptible to certain stimuli. These stimuli may be primary stimuli releasing and directing internal impulses. The instinctive mechanism responds to these impulses by co-ordinated movements which contribute to the maintenance of the individual, and thereafter to the maintenance of the species.

## Releasers

Certain theories exist in connection with releasers. A releaser is defined as any specific feature in an animal's environment which prompts an instinctive response. Characters which are peculiar to individuals of a given species can thus set in motion definite chains of instinctive actions. The theory of the innate releasing mechanism (IRM) has grown from this hypothesis. The innate releasing mechanism is considered to be a physiological mechanism, built into the animal and inactive until such time as it becomes appropriately stimulated. The 'biologically-right' stimulus in the environment is considered to be the key which unlocks the appropriate behaviour pattern. Releasers act upon the IRM by issuing a simple sign stimulus. The environment holds many releasers for animal behaviour. One particular type of releaser which plays an important part in determining behaviour is the social releaser. A social releaser is either a device of colour or shape, a sequence of movements, varieties of sounds or a general scene which has the specific function of eliciting a particular response in another member of the same species. The perceptual correlate to the releaser is the IRM.

# DISPLACEMENT ACTIVITIES

These constitute an important category of behaviour and they bear some resemblance to instinctive behaviour. A displacement activity is seen as an incomplete or imperfectly oriented form of behaviour. Typically, it is produced by the animal out of the customary context of its behaviour pattern. The displaced activity is not seen related to its normal pattern. It occurs as the result of sidetracking of the energy behind the activity. Such activities are considered to be due to the animal finding itself unable to inhibit an aroused impulse, and having to express the energy of the impulse in some other way. Displacement activities result typically from the activation of one or more drives which cannot be expressed at the moment of their stimulation. The mechanism of a displacement activity has been described as the sparking over of a drive from one channel to another.

Displacement activities appear as irrelevant behavioural episodes, but a number of recent studies by modern ethologists have shown that many displacement activities are not quite as irrelevant as was once thought. It is now believed that displacement activities have three principal characteristics:

1. For their production they require equilibrium between the two conflicting drives, that is to say, the two tendencies which are in conflict should be comparable in strength.

2. This equilibrium between the two conflicting drives must persist in the animal long enough for the displacement activity to be organized and displayed.

3. There must be adequate external stimuli, for the displacement activity itself to be shown by the animal. Displacement activities are by no means uncommon in farm animal behaviour, and their manifestation can be taken as evidence that the animal is being thwarted by its environment.

## IMPRINTING AND LEARNING

The theory of imprinting is an important one in ethology. Imprinting is considered to result when a young animal at an impressionable age (while the learning threshold is low) is exposed to a meaningful stimulus. This then is a learning mechanism, although its presence as a mechanism is innately predetermined. Imprinting affects the very young animal and, normally at such times in its early neonatal life, involves the recognition of its dam and its essential behavioural attachment to the dam. The stimulus that becomes imprinted at such times initiates behaviour that persists throughout the remainder of the animal's life, and indeed, may dominate many other activities that it might subsequently learn.

Characteristically, imprinting is a rapid and very stable form of learning and it appears to be effective even without elaborate reinforcement. The young individual learns the principal characteristics of the species to which it belongs as well as those of its own dam. These principal characteristics are subsequently used by the individual at a more mature age as releasers.

The processes of learning are important in determining the ultimate behaviour of animals. Unlearned patterns of behaviour, which constitute the manifestation of instincts, become exhibited less often as animals become older and acquire experience. With age, learning accumulates and in time learned responses come to dominate the earlier unlearned ones. The rate of learning in the maturing animal is an accelerating one.

Learning may accumulate in a number of differing ways. The simplest form is the adoption of those behavioural responses which the animal finds appropriate to the stimulation. The early process of learning in the newborn animal is based largely on trial and error. Learning also occurs in animals when they observe other animals with which they are in association. After observing the behaviour of the others, younger animals may attempt to repeat these actions themselves. This is learning by the process of mimesis. Mimesis is the portrayal of imitated behaviour patterns. By this imitation process young animals learn a great deal of their feeding behaviour from their dams, even before weaning. Other behavioural features, such as the display of oestrus in some females, are also apparently improved in time with mimesis. Another important method of learning in animals is the development of conditioned reflexes.

## Conditioning

In the process of conditioning a response in the animal's behaviour, which has already been the result of a given stimulus, becomes adapted in response to a change of stimulus; the second stimulus being different from the one which was originally effective. The original or primary stimulus is termed the unconditioned stimulus. In time the unconditioned stimulus becomes replaced by the conditioned stimulus in many practical circumstances; but sometimes the animal becomes conditioned not to make a response that it was already accustomed to making to a given stimulus. Conditioning of this negative type is fundamental in the establishment of inhibitions in animal behaviour.

In conditioning, a state of generalization is recognized. In this state, actions occur in a great variety of circumstances, which are unrelated or may only have a loose connection with the primary stimulus. The Pavlovian term for this phenomenon is irradiation of excitation. The phenomenon explains a certain amount of abnormal behaviour among animals.

## THE CONCEPT OF DRIVE

An animal's motivation can often be deduced by its behaviour. When behaviour leads to an indisputably recognizable goal the motivation is identifiable. Motivation stems from the blending together of numerous items, such as stimulating factors and the animal's bodily properties such as experience, inheritance and current physiological status. These various elements obviously include innate ones, but all may blend variably and motivational change results. No matter how it may be changed, motivation often exhibits specific direction. In ethology certain specific motivations are termed drives. Because of the clarity of motivation, through the easy detection of goal or intent, the sexual, maternal and feeding drives are those principally acknowledged. Other minor drives may be recognizable, including the drives of play and exploration. The concept of drive is useful in ethology in that it organizes some of the descriptive theory of the subject. It must be understood that the term drive exists only as a concept and that it lacks substance. In ethology, care must be taken not to extend the applications of this term beyond its obvious and generally accepted validity. The term must not be used to explain away miscellaneous behavioural phenomena, since such an explanation of behaviour is no explanation at all. Whilst explanations are sought by ethologists, factual ones are now preferred to hypothetical ones.

Acceptance of the concept of drive allows us to recognize many of the individual factors contributing to 'driven' behaviour. Changes in levels of drive are to be seen under certain typical circumstances of season and husbandry. Variations in drive among individuals can be observed, and these draw attention to innate factors in behaviour and the role of genes. Such observations will deservedly draw more attention to inheritance and evolution in animal behaviour.

The *sex drives* in both sexes are manifest in a vast array of behavioural features which will be described and discussed in later sections of this book. Essentially, the sex drive depends on a given level (threshold) of sex hormone being produced and acting on the neural tissues in the presence of appropriate environmental stimulation. Specific centres in the central nervous systems have been recognized as being totally concerned with sexual behaviour, but the mechanisms are very imperfectly understood in farm animals. The production of the sex hormones by the gonads is, however, satisfactorily understood as this is an area of endocrinology which has fascinated researchers for a long time. The effects of these hormones in their very small quantities are nothing if not impressive.

The neural–chemical basis of the *maternal drive* is poorly and inadequately understood and remains speculative and conceptual.

The hunger or *feeding drive* has a physiological basis which is quite well understood. Evidently hunger is derived principally from the actions of opposing hunger and satiety centres located in the hypothalamic region of the brain. These centres operate on the basis of information brought along nerve tracts from the gut and the glucose levels in circulating blood. These centres control food intake and body weight; damage to them causes abnormally excessive or deficient appetite.


# THE CONCEPT OF STRESS

Stress cannot be ignored in a study of farm animal behaviour. Many would consider it to be the main justification for the emergence of this subject as a speciality. It has been suggested, and is widely accepted, that behavioural change may be the principal identifiable evidence of stress in farm animals. Many veterinarians now accept that when an animal fails to adapt to its environment, abnormal behaviour results. At present there is certainly no other satisfactory indicator of stress. This is regrettable since domestication in general, and intensive husbandry of farm animals in particular, provide limited opportunities for animals to adapt to their special physical environments.

A considerable variety of meanings have been applied to stress as a concept in spite of (and because of) the very great volume of study and research which has been devoted to the subject. Some common ground does exist, however, despite the disagreements. The view that stress is an external force is the most common, erroneous one. Stress is not the external factor impinging on the complex adaptive apparatus of the animal; it is the state of the latter apparatus resulting from stressors issuing from the environment of the animal. Heat stress, for example, is the syndrome of hyperthermia in the animal, not the temperature of its ambient environment. Many environmental features clearly possess stressing capacities for animals in confinement. Unfavourable ambient temperature and husbandry conditions including food supply, stock density and space allocation can easily defy adaptation and create stress in an animal.

Very much remains to be learned about the behavioural product resulting from stress in farm animals, but an earnest start has been made.

# SUPPLEMENTARY READING

ARMSTRONG, E. A. (1950) The nature and function of displacement activities. In: *Physiological Mechanisms in Animal Behaviour. Symposium of the Society for Experimental Biology. No. IV*, ed. R. Brown & J. F. Danielli. Cambridge: Cambridge University Press.

ASCHOFF, J. (1964) Survival value of diurnal rhythms. In: *The Biology of Survival. Symposia of the Zoological Society of London. No. 13*, ed. O. G. Edholm, pp. 79–98. London: Zoological Society (distributed by Academic Press, New York).

CARTHY, J. D. & EBLING, F. T. (1964) *The Natural History of Aggression.* New York: Academic Press.

GOY, R. W. & JALSWOY, J. S. (1962) Role of inheritance in determination of sexual behavior patterns. In: *Roots of Behavior*, ed. E. L. Bliss, pp. 96–110. New York: Harper Bros.

HARKER, J. E. (1964) Diurnal rhythms and homeostatic mechanisms. In: *Homeostasis and Feedback Mechanisms. Symposia of the Society for*

*Experimental Biology. No. XVIII*, ed. G. M. Hughes, pp. 283–300. New York: Academic Press.

MOLTZ, H. (1971) *The Ontogeny of Vertebrate Behavior*. New York and London: Academic Press.

SPURWOY, H. (1956) *Cultural Mammalogy. New Biology No. 20*, pp. 104–111. Harmondsworth: Penguin.

TINBERGEN, N. (1948) Social releasers and the experimental method required for their study. *Wilson Bull., 60*, 6.

TINBERGEN, N. (1951) *The Study of Instinct*. Oxford: Clarendon Press.

# 3.

# Physiological Ethology

AN ANIMAL'S behaviour is the result of the complexity of interactions which take place between it and its environment. It is to be seen as the overt and composite functioning of the whole animal—a definition which has already been offered in this book. Early in the study of behaviour then, it is necessary to look at some of the mechanisms by which animals function, namely, their physiological processes. In reviewing the principal physiological features of ethological consequence, foremost attention must be paid to the role of sense organs and the neural and endocrine mechanisms.

## STIMULATION

The operation of the sense organs is dependent upon the reception of stimulation.

Most behaviour is the result of stimulation which has originated in an animal's immediate environment. This stimulation principally affects the individual through its sensory apparatus in various ways.

### *Tactile Stimulation*

This is one form which is ever present in the animal. The importance of tactile sensitivity is recognized in some of the principal behavioural activities, including breeding and nursing. Tactile stimulation between the sexes is a vital factor in the mating of farm animals. Again tactile interchanges between mother and young are a type of exchange for ensuring their mutual recognition and tolerance. Through tactile stimulation an animal receives a subconscious impression of its immediate environment. For the animal to be in harmony with its immediate environment, to ensure satisfactory resting behaviour for example, it is clear that tactile sensation must be appropriate.

Some tactile sensations are clearly pleasant to animals. Grooming activities, for example, are largely concerned with the exchange of tactile sensation between pairs of animals. Individual grooming activities also depend upon the reverberation of the tactile sensory apparatus. While grooming behaviour can be considered to be the means of obtaining some degree of skin hygiene, it must also be realized that it is an activity which must be performed properly for an animal to be in close harmony with its environment.

## Olfactory Stimulation

It is becoming abundantly clear that the sense of olfaction is of critical importance in the stimulation of a wide variety of responses in animals. Reproductive responses, for example, are quite evidently under the control of the olfactory senses to a very large extent. Odour can be seen to have a stimulatory value in arousing the male sex drive; a simple and obvious manifestation of this is to be seen in the olfactory reflex which was originally termed flehmen (the German term). Flehmen is usually observed in male animals immediately after nosing the genital regions of females, but it is also sometimes noticed in females after nosing newborn and their own offspring.

Odorous substances eliminated by one animal which have the specific effect of stimulating another animal, usually of the opposite sex, are termed pheromones. The importance of the role of pheromones in the breeding behaviour of animals is becoming much more widely acknowledged. These pheromones have various sites of production and routes of elimination. For example, they are produced in the preputial fluids of the boar. There are a variety of male animal odours which are detectable even to man; the smell of the billy goat, for instance, is almost certainly pheromonal in its effect on female members of the same species.

The production and the reception of odour clearly are important in generating behaviour. Odour plays a large part in the establishment of the strong bonds between a mother and the newborn animal. These bonds are dependent firstly on mutual recognition through odour. As the association continues the reception of the appropriate odour acts as a stimulant to the nursing process of milk let-down and vigorous sucking in the infant animal. It is commonly observed that a dam which is nursing a young animal

24

will turn around to nose the hindquarters of the nursling and apparently confirm its identity by odour (Fig. 1). The accidental acquisition of alien odours by young animals as a result of them being handled by people are known to have unfortunate effects in the form of maternal rejection.

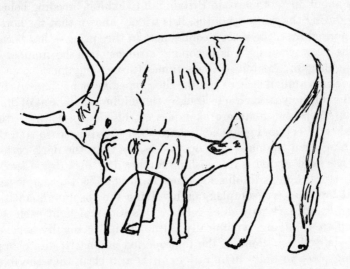

Fig. 1. Cow and newborn calf in the typical bigeminal formation which facilitates the stimulatory cycle in nursing/suckling. (tracing) (See also the mediaeval illustration on the front cover.)

## Visual Stimulation

This is the most potent one of all in determining farm animal behaviour. Recognition of territory, associates, food and handlers are all principally determined by the sense of sight, the use of which engages an animal's activity most of the time. Visual stimulation is also important in breeding activities since certain female animals appear to have certain stimulant properties for certain sires. Although odour is the principal means by which early recognition occurs between mother and young, visual recognition soon takes over as the secondary means of mutual identification.

It has been known for some time that the relative length of the light period of each day is a factor in determining breeding behaviour in farm animals. Seasonal breeding, for instance, is largely determined by the changes in the daily photoperiod. Photo-periodism operates in two principal ways:

1. Some animals exhibit their reproductive activities during that portion of the year during which the daily light period is long. Horses are an example of this. Although it is thought that only about 50% of mares in Britain fail to exhibit breeding behaviour during the winter months, it is widely known that for horses the normal breeding season commences in the spring—that period of the year when light is becoming stronger and the number of daylight hours greater—and continues through summer.

2. Some animal species confine their breeding behaviour to that portion of the year characterized by the minimum amount of daily light; sheep and goats are examples of this. Most of the British breeds of sheep and goats commence their breeding seasons in the autumn when the daily photoperiod is less than the dark period, and the light period is diminishing further day after day. Clearly, the natural light stimulus for those farm animals that show seasonal breeding is a complex one involving the absolute quantities of light and dark as well as relative quantities of light each day which are changing dynamically. Although it is generally believed that daily fluctuations in the photoperiod emphasize the change taking place in daily light rations, it is also clear that the fixed nature of the photoperiod is important, i.e. seasonal breeding animals maintain their breeding activities as long as an adequate quantity of light (or of dark) is delivered. When the photoperiod fails to provide adequate stimulation for the animal a refractory period develops during which the breeding performance is arrested.

## Auditory Stimulation

Vocal communication between animals is an effective method of stimulating behaviour in the social and sexual fields. As evidence of this, it is noticeable how much difference there is in vocal characteristics. Vocal expression by animals ensures that auditory stimuli are being exchanged. Auditory stimulation has been studied in horses and pigs. In the latter species most study has probably been devoted to the effect of auditory stimulation on breeding. It has been found that the 'chant de coeur' by the boar is frequently a prerequisite to breeding responses in the sow. These sounds from the boar have also been noted to be specific for this purpose.

There is abundant evidence that auditory stimulation plays a large part in maintaining the close bond between dam and the newborn animal which is essential for the satisfactory nourishment of the latter, particularly in the early days of its life. Clearly animals react to auditory stimulation of a great variety of types. They show alarm in response to certain sounds while other sounds produce an evidently reassuring effect. Distressing auditory stimulation can accumulate to the point where it is of traumatic effect, and farm animals in the presence of a great quantity of unacceptable and alien sounds will usually show behaviour which indicates disharmony with their environment.

## Gustatory Stimulation

This also plays a part in determining behaviour. Insufficient attention has, in the past, been devoted to the manner in which animals select their food. Under free-living conditions, animals employ a good deal of selectivity in feeding. Under domestication they may not always be given the opportunity to exercise this form of discrimination in feeding. Thus it is of even greater importance in domestication to ensure that palatable foods are provided for animals so that the optimum uptake of expensively compounded feeds is assured.

Gustatory clues are used by females at the time of parturition in recognizing their own offspring. Immediately following the birth process the farm animals typically show intensive grooming activities towards their neonates. This takes the form of nibbling and licking over the surface of the moist newly-born animal. In the course of this grooming, gustatory clues are received; these play a part in the complex identity which the newborn acquires for its own dam.

Gustatory stimulation also appears to play an important part in grazing behaviour and ensures that the requisite chemical elements are consumed by an animal in appropriate quantities to maintain health. Animals suffering from various forms of nutritional deficiencies usually first give evidence of this by abnormal feeding activities which indicate that palatability has been altered for them.

# THE NERVOUS SYSTEM

The chief functions of the brain, spinal cord and peripheral nerves is the production of behaviour. Information about internal and external factors concerning an animal passes to the central nervous system through a range of receptors. Stimulation affects the animal's sensory receptors and may be varied in nature. It can be chemical, thermal or mechanical. The sense organs convey a received stimulus to the peripheral nerves which in their turn produce the phenomenon of excitation. When stimuli have been built up to an adequate level they provide a train of nerve impulses which are waves of electrical activity sweeping along the surface of the individual nerve fibres. Nerve impulses are of the same charge at all times but differ in their frequency. When the stimuli increase in strength the frequency of the impulses increases, and although responses are not constantly related to the impulse they nevertheless tend to be.

The receptors which provide information for the nervous system are of two main types; these are the exteroceptors and the interoceptors. Exteroceptors deal with stimulation originating outside the animal. They include the receptors found in the skin as well as the organs of vision, hearing and smell. The latter organs are sometimes referred to as teleceptors since they can deal with stimuli originating some considerable distance from the animal. Interoceptors are concerned with stimulation originating within the body. These receptors are located within muscles, joints, tendons and internal organs.

Receptors which provide nervous impulses giving rise to sensations in the animal are known as sense organs. The principal sense organs in determining animal behaviour include the organs of sight, smell and hearing. Other receptors create impulses which do not reach consciousness but nevertheless produce reflexes. Such receptors are called activators.

Of fundamental importance to the transmission of impulses through the nervous system is the synapse. When an impulse passing along a nerve fibre reaches the fibre's end and meets another neurone (or nerve cell), it crosses over at a synapse. Synapses are the points of contact between neurones. Trains of impulses arriving at a synapse are passed on if they are of sufficient frequency. The function of the synapse is to control neural transmissions, limiting cross-communications between nervous tracts. Some synapses have an inhibitory effect on nerve signals. Synapses connect neurones to form specific neural pathways. In many cases the neural paths lead to the cerebral cortex which is the outer covering of the cerebrum.

## Cerebral Cortex

The cerebral cortex, although acting as a unit, has certain localized regions where sensory impulses are received and subjected to redirection. These specialized areas of the cortex are primary sites for sensory reception, the nervous activity subsequently spreading over a greater area. The cortex has a multitude of cells and neural paths, each one communicating with many others. This extremely complex relay system permits tremendous variability in the way that nerve impulses may be channelled.

The cerebral cortex possesses four main sensory areas into which projectory fibres discharge. These are:
1. The somasthetic or body sense area
2. The visual area
3. The auditory area
4. The olfactory area

All of these are important in the receipt and interpretation of nerve signals, and are fundamental in determining behaviour.

*The somasthetic area.* This area is sited in the parietal lobe of the cortex and receives nerve impulses from very many parts of the body including its surface.

*The visual area.* Nerve fibres are collected from the retina of the eye into the optic nerves and are distributed, within the cortex, to the extensive visual area at the occipital part of the cerebrum. Recognition of patterns and releasers takes place in the visual area.

*The auditory area.* This is located in the temporal lobe of the cerebral cortex. The area receives nerve impulses concerned with auditory sensations from the thalamus. The fibres of the hearing nerve end in the pons, from which region other fibres pass to the thalamus and then to the cortex.

*The olfactory area.* The sensory area dealing with smell plays a much more important role in breeding behaviour than has generally been recognized. An olfactory region is located in the hippocampus which receives projection fibres from the centre in the olfactory bulb. This centre deals with olfactory reflexes. The fibres of the olfactory system originate with nerve cells located in the mucous membrane of the nasal passages and terminate within the olfactory bulbs.

Nerve impulses are also received into the brain via the reticular activating system which transmits signals concerned with fundamental physiological affairs. The dorsal columns of spinal nerves convey impulses received from touch receptors on the surface of the animal's body.

## The Hypothalamus

A highly complex convergence of nervous influence occurs in the hypothalamic area. The hypothalamus is also influenced by informative material brought to it in the circulation. The receipt of afferent stimulation gives the hypothalamus the role of maintaining and regulating the activity of the pituitary gland.

The cerebral cortex interrelates closely with the hypothalamus. Some regions of the cortex communicate directly with the hypothalamus, these are the 'old brain' regions, e.g. the areas of the frontal lobe and of the orbital frontal regions. Various parts of the forebrain convey neural activities to the hypothalamus through a variety of systems, either directly or after interruptions, so that by one route or another it is in receipt of impulses from optic, olfactory, acoustic, tactile and internal sources. These sensory stimuli can enter the brain from all directions: anteriorly through the optic nerve, laterally through the cochlear part of the acoustic nerve behind the pons and posteriorly through the dorsal columns of the cord.

The routes to the hypothalamus are by no means direct in all cases. Sensory stimulations arising in the genitalia, for example, travel via spinal nerves to the cord and pass along to the brain via the dorsal column. It is at the level of the hypothalamus that patterns of nervous activities become integrated and regulated so as to establish the adaptive reactions of the animal. Even behaviour which is largely dependent upon experience and learning in the animal is seldom, if ever, completely free of control by the primitive mechanisms established in the hypothalamus and in the subcortex generally. The neural links involving the subcortex and the links between the hypothalamus and the surrounding brain in particular, remain the principal integrators of most behavioural patterns.

The limbic system, located deep in the subcortex, apparently contains neural centres such as the amygdala which control aggressive behaviour in its various forms.

The working units of the hypothalamus are neurones which are grouped into 'nuclei'. These nuclei operate together in a fashion resembling a computer. The information from various levels of the brain is received and processed by these nuclei before signals are subsequently re-issued to more specialized parts of the body, which are geared to function under the control of the hypothalamus. Much of the influence of hypothalamic activity is directed at the production of hormones in the subjacent pituitary gland. The pituitary is the principal endocrine gland in the body and its hormonal production is all important in the maintenance of the bulk of the body's activities, including behaviour. Even the all important central hypothalamus is responsive to some of the endocrine activity for which it is initially responsible. Quite recently it has become clear that there is probably a considerable amount of hormonal control over the hypothalamus. It appears that this is sometimes due to the influence of hormones indirectly acting via the surface of the cerebrum (the cerebral cortex).

It seems that areas of the cortex are so designed as to correlate dynamically with receptive areas on the body's surface. The neural importance of the superficial area and central nervous areas changes according to the major activities of an animal; for example, it seems that the appropriate area of the cortex is more receptive to stimulation from the genitalia during breeding times. The hypothalamus in its turn becomes informed of such neural changes and the hypothalamic cells, which are normally slow-firing and discharging slow trains of impulses, change to a faster firing rate. The firing rate of the cells in the hypothalamus does not increase in response to stimulation of the genitalia when the animal concerned is not in an active breeding phase and when its sex hormone level is low. Experimental studies have also indicated that the maternal subject shows a much more active hypothalamus when the let-down of milk has been stimulated by the nursling animal. These nursing activities seem capable of quickly producing conspicuous acceleration in the firing rate of hypothalamic cells.

# THE ENDOCRINE SYSTEM

A knowledge of endocrinology—the functional activities of the endocrine system—is vital to a study of ethology because of the great effect which the endocrine glands have through their production of hormones, upon the sundry activities of the body. The endocrine system has certain advantages over the nervous system resulting from its ability to convey information and instructions to the body, throughout all cells, via the blood circulation. The steady production of hormones provides a method of maintaining a constant and prolonged signal for specific parts of the body to obey. In addition fluctuations in output may influence the body's internal state and often cause behavioural changes. The nervous system and the endocrine system are clearly adapted for different roles but contact between them is essential for their full function since they are interdependent. The two systems co-operate with each other through the processes of neural secretion and through the effects of hormones on the brain.

Hormone secretion is subject to the influence of many forms of stimulation. External stimuli have a great influence on hormone production and, as has already been noted, one such form of external stimulus is the photoperiod. It is also known that a variety of other forms of stimulation received by an animal in the course of social and other activities have the effect of promoting endocrine activity. Functional endocrinology now recognizes an elaborate organization of interactions between the animal's own activity, the external stimuli which it receives and its internal physiological state. Any of these three factors—behaviour, environment and internal state—can alter in force to cause a change in the others. This elaborate apparatus clearly creates a potentially complex situation.

To obtain some understanding of this complex mechanism the function of the individual endocrine glands requires examination at this stage.

## The Pituitary Gland

The pituitary gland is of first importance since it exercises a primary role through its control of other endocrine glands which are, in their turn, secondary within the endocrine system.

The pituitary gland, consisting of two separate regions—the anterior and the posterior lobes—is suspended from a stalk at the base of the brain, at the rear of the cranium and is closely connected to the hypothalamic region. The hypothalamus has, as we have already learned, a singular importance in controlling endocrine affairs through its control of the pituitary. A nerve tract originating in the hypothalamus runs through the pituitary stalk to feed the posterior lobe, while the anterior lobe of the pituitary gland only communicates with the hypothalamus through a portal system of blood vessels. This establishes a direct link between the hypothalamus and its cells and the pituitary gland.

The two portions of the pituitary gland produce and secrete specific hormones which act as chemical messengers circulating to other endocrine glands in particular, and to distant parts of the body, known in this context as target organs, which may in their turn produce their own hormones.

Of great importance in reproductive behaviour is the output of the gonadotropic hormones from the anterior pituitary. These hormones are the luteinizing hormone (LH) and the follicle stimulating hormone (FSH) which are produced in the male and in the female in concert, and influence the activities in the respective gonads, viz. the testicle or the ovary.

In the female, the two hormones, although produced together, dominate each other alternately; this gives rise to the cyclic activity of reproduction characteristic of the female. In the male animal, however, the production of these two hormones appears to be level and continuous.

Another hormone produced by the pituitary gland is prolactin, and although its role has become uncertain in the light of present knowledge, it is known to be largely responsible in evolving maternal behaviour.

The posterior pituitary gland produces oxytocin. This important hormone is responsible for various uterine activities and also the release of milk in the lactating animal. It is this hormone which encourages the outflow of milk at suckling. Oxytocin is produced in the maternal subject in response to nerve signals received following tactile stimulatory behaviour in her mammary region on the part of nursling animals. Visual and other stimuli are also provided by the nursling's appearance and behaviour. Sexual stimulation of the male is also known to be attributable to oxytocin production.

## *The Thyroid Gland*

One of the glands influenced by the pituitary is the thyroid gland and the hormone which it produces is termed thyroxine. This is closely involved in most of the body's activities concerning energy output and therefore affects behaviour in general. The steady production of thyroxine is important in maintaining regular maternal activities, female cyclic sexual activities and sex drive in both sexes.

## *The Adrenal Gland*

The adrenal glands—one adherent to each kidney—produce steroid substances in their outer cortices. Production is a consequence of hormonal stimulation from the pituitary gland. In the male, these steroid substances are termed androgens. Androgens are the male hormones, and those from the adrenal act in support of the principal male hormone produced in the testis. The effect of adrenal hormones on sexual activity must be considerable, however, since it is known that disease of the adrenal cortex can cause marked alterations in sexual behaviour through altered production of adrenal hormones.

The central portion of the adrenal gland, namely the medulla, is the region in which adrenaline is produced. The sudden release of adrenaline into the circulation is associated with marked sudden changes in behaviour. Threat behaviour, flight behaviour and behaviour combining these, such as the fight or flight reaction, all result from a sudden increase in adrenaline production. Again a sudden increase in adrenaline output results in agonistic behaviour in general, and is likely to promote forms of behaviour such as fighting, among male animals, and maternal protective behaviour. Adrenaline provides the basis of all the alarm reactions, and it is also known that increased adrenaline output arrests the flow of milk in the suckling animal. Some release of adrenaline from the medulla of the adrenal gland proceeds almost continuously, but sudden increases in its secretion are known to result from disturbing stimuli in the immediate environment of the subject.

## The Sex Organs

*The Testis*. The testis of the mature male secretes testosterone, the principal hormone responsible for most of the typically male behaviour. It seems that the level of production is not of critical importance since an increased supply of the hormone does not necessarily result in increased sexual activities. It has been found that if the production of testosterone is sufficient for normal behavioural responses of male type, then overproduction of the hormone does not modify sexual behaviour. Obviously there can be very little effective male sex behaviour in the absence of testosterone. In those species where there are seasonal fluctuations in the expression of male sex drive, such as rams, there is a corresponding cycle in the production of testosterone.

*The Ovary*. In the female animal the ovary is the source of oestrogen, the hormone responsible for female sexual behaviour. The ripened follicle of the ovary which precedes ovulation is the principal source of this ovarian hormone. The follicular cells increase in size rapidly just before oestrus. At this time the output of oestrogen increases greatly. Once the oestrogen in the animal's circulation has reached a threshold level all the behavioural signs of oestrus typical of that species are shown. Oestrous behaviour is maintained for the period during which the follicle is at the peak of its maturity, but when ovulation occurs with the bursting of the follicle a sharp drop in oestrogen production occurs and oestrous behaviour ceases.

*Hormone levels*. With both oestrogen and testosterone, there is no clear relationship between the quantity of hormone and the intensity of the sexual behaviour shown. An adequate level of oestrogen in the body will only ensure that oestrous behaviour will be exhibited. The degree to which this behaviour will be shown is not dependent on the hormonal level, but is principally under the control of inherited nervous factors. In both sexes a feedback mechanism operates between the hypothalamus and the gonad. The level of sex hormone produced by the gonad is communicated to the hypothalamus. The hypothalamus is capable of reducing the endocrine activity of the gonad if the level of sex hormone becomes excessive; likewise, if the level of sex hormone is insufficient, the hypothalamus can quickly stimulate the pituitary into increased gonadotropic output.

## The Pineal Gland

The pineal is a very small endocrine gland located deep in the brain and directly above the hypothalamus. In some lower forms of animal life this gland is known as the 'third eye'. In the large farm animals the pineal gland produces a hormone called melatonin. Melatonin appears to control cyclic breeding behaviour. It is evidently under the control of light stimuli and is, therefore a form of third eye even in mammals. Certainly oestrous behaviour in animals requires melatonin production, and melatonin in its turn requires the stimulation from light and dark phases.

## Hormones in General

It has been well-known that hormones exercise a great deal of control over behaviour. Today, the improved knowledge of endocrinology justifies this general belief by showing the many ways in which hormone production takes place in animals. In many cases this production is under external influences and ultimately dictates that behaviour which is appropriate for an animal in its own environment.

## SUPPLEMENTARY READING

AMOROSO, E. C. & MARSHALL, F. H. A. (1960) External factors in sexual periodicity. In: *Marshall's Physiology of Reproduction*, ed. A. S. Parkes, 3rd ed., chapter 13. Harlow: Longmans Green.
CANNON, W. B. (1953) *Bodily Changes in Pain, Hunger, Fear and Rage*. Boston: Brandford Co.
CROSS, B. A. (1964) The hypothalamus in mammalian homeostasis.

In: *Homeostasis and Feedback Mechanisms. Symposia of the Society for Experimental Biology. No. XVIII*, ed. G. M. Hughes, pp. 157–193. New York: Academic Press.

EMMENS, C. W. (1959) Role of gonadal hormones in reproductive processes. In: *Reproduction in Domestic Animals*, ed. H. H. Cole & P. T. Cupps, vol. 1, chapter 4. New York: Academic Press.

GOY, R. W. & PHOENIX, C. H. (1963) Hypothalamic regulation of female sexual behaviour. *J. Reprod. Fert.*, *5*, 23–40.

LEHRMAN, D. S. (1962) Interaction of hormonal and experiential influences on development of behavior. In: *Roots of Behavior*, ed. E. L. Bliss, pp. 142–156. New York: Harper Bros.

MAYER, W. & GELDER, R. Van. (1965) *Physiological Mammalogy (Volume 11)*. London: Academic Press.

ORTAVANT, R., MAULEON, P. & THIBAULT, C. (1964) Photoperiodic control of gonadal and hypophyseal activity in domestic mammals. *Ann. N.Y. Acad. Sci.*, *117*, 157–193.

PARKES, A. S. & BRUCE, H. M. (1961) Olfactory stimuli in mammalian reproduction. *Science*, *134*, 1049–1054.

ROWLANDS, I. W. ed. (1966) *Comparative Biology of Reproduction in Mammals. Symposia of the Zoological Society of London, No. 15*. London: Zoological Society (distributed by Academic Press, New York).

SCHNEIRLA, T. C. (1965) Approach/withdrawal and behaviour. In: *Advances in the Study of Behaviour*, ed. D. S. Lehrman, R. A. Hinde & E. Shaw, pp. 1–74. New York: Academic Press.

SCOTT, J. P. (1962) Hostility and aggression in animals. In: *Roots of Behavior*, ed. E. L. Bliss, pp. 167–178. New York: Harper Bros.

TANSLEY, K. (1950) Vision. In: *Physiological Mechanisms in Animal Behaviour. Symposium of the Society for Experimental Biology. No. IV*, ed. R. Brown & J. F. Danielli. Cambridge: Cambridge University Press.

YEATES, N. T. M. (1954) Daylight changes. In: *Recent Progress in the Physiology of Farm Animals*, ed. J. Hammond, vol. 1, p. 363. London: Butterworths.

YOUNG, W. C. (1957) Genetic and psychological determination of sexual behavior patterns. In: *Hormones, Brain Function and Behavior*, ed. Hudson Hoagland, pp. 75–98. New York: Academic Press.

# Part II
# BEHAVIOUR PATTERNS

# 4.

# Behaviour Patterns in Horses

## LOCOMOTION

Locomotion in the horse may take one of four different forms. These gaits can be distinguished by the sequences in which the hooves are lifted from the ground, and alter with the acceleration of speed from the walk, through the trot, to the canter and thence the gallop.

The canter and the gallop are mechanically identical in their hoof-lifting sequences, but differ in rate of performance or speed; the gallop being an accelerated canter. At slowest speed, i.e. the walk, the sequence of hoof lifting proceeds as follows: near hind, near fore, off hind, off fore. This is repeated with a return to near hind. In the trot the animal is balanced alternately on diagonally opposite feet, and the sequence of hoof lifting is as follows: near fore with off hind, off fore with near hind. This is repeated with a return to near fore with off hind. In the gallop the horse uses the same action at maximum speed, but at one point there is a floating phase during which all four feet are collected under the body and are off the ground. When the off forelimb throws the horse into this floating phase it is termed an off-leg lead, when the near forelimb throws the horse into the floating phase it is, conversely, a near-leg lead. A typical sequence of feet movements in the gallop is as follows: off fore, floating phase, near hind, off hind, near fore. This sequence is followed by a return to off fore. With a near-leg lead, the sequence is as follows: near fore, floating phase, off hind, near hind, off fore. In the gallop there are never more than two feet on the ground together. In the canter, however, both hind feet are still on the ground when the first forefoot touches the ground.

During locomotion, horses are capable of effecting quite spectacular jumps, both in distance and height covered. Few horses, however, jump often until they are taught to jump, and indeed untaught horses may avoid obstacles only 60 cm high rather than

41

clear them by jumping. Normally horses avoid jumping over ditches. They show a vertical reluctance to jump over horizontal obstacles.

## RESTING AND SLEEP

When the horse lies down all the legs are gathered together under the body, the knees and hocks are bent and the chest and forequarters make contact with the ground before the hindquarters. The adult horse normally rests slightly on one side of its chest with one foreleg and one hind leg underneath the body. On rising, the horse stretches out both forelegs raising first the forequarters, and then the remainder of the body on its hind feet. Adult horses do not lie for very long periods. Mares with young foals tend to lie longer than usual when the foal is near by and sleeping in full lateral recumbency. Mature horses are unable to lie in this flat out posture for long periods of time before their respiratory functions become impaired. The full weight on the thorax of the horse, when laid flat, appears to be such that circulation to the lungs becomes inefficient after about 15 minutes. This is not the case among foals and young horses, however, and these subjects can be seen to spend many hours in the day sleeping on their sides at full stretch.

Many horses accumulate 6 to 7 hours of sleep during each 24-hour period. Some of this sleep is accumulated during the hours of daylight and it is largely achieved in the standing position. Typically, periods of sleep are short and irregularly spaced with rest. No regular patterns of resting or sleeping have been observed in adult horses.

It is unusual to see all the members of a group of horses lying down simultaneously. Knowledge of normal lying and resting behaviour in horses was inadequate in the past and led to some unsatisfactory methods of securing animals in recumbent positions for surgical intervention. For example, a horse naturally never lies on its back except when grooming itself, but when placed in this position for surgery it soon suffers from the effects of pulmonary stasis. Again, when a horse is cast and subsequently rolled in order to place it for the surgeon, it is not always remembered that when the horse rolls naturally it normally pauses in midroll with all four

Fig. 2. Horse in midroll. This position is maintained momentarily while the back is worked against the ground. The midroll allows internal organs to catch up with the turn and so prevents twisting of the gut. (tracing)

feet in the air momentarily (Fig. 2). Quick or hasty rolling, especially in large animals and those with very full intestines can create a fatal gut twist.

# EXPLORATION

A great deal of exploratory behaviour is shown by the newborn foal. This behaviour is directed towards the pasture, the ground, the premises and their boundaries and other objects in the environment within its touch. In the course of this exploratory activity the foal may nibble and mouth unfamiliar objects. Such keen exploratory behaviour is not shown to the same degree in adult horses, except between themselves. They, nevertheless, acquire familiarity with allocated territory, and familiar territory is evidently quickly adopted as the home range. Horses use eliminative behaviour to a large extent in defining their territory, and the home range becomes marked and mapped out by deposits of excreta. Preference for the home range is very strong among horses and they typically show more willingness to be moved towards home than away from home.

# INGESTION

Horses graze by cropping the pasture close to the roots with their incisors. Whilst grazing they cover large areas and seldom take more than two mouthfuls before moving at least one step further on, avoiding grass patches covered in excreta. They maintain some distance between each other when grazing in groups.

The young foal does not graze very efficiently until it is several weeks old. By about the end of the first week of life, however, the foal has begun to nibble the herbage in association with its dam. Horses have been seen to spend some time vigorously de-barking trees, but the reason for this apparently aberrant form of eating behaviour is as yet unknown.

Horses do not drink very frequently in a 24-hour period and many may only drink once a day. When they do drink they typically consume very large quantities of water, totalling up to fifteen to twenty swallows.

# ELIMINATION

While horses are emptying their excreta storage organs, bladder and rectum, they usually cease other body activities. Stallions show careful and deliberate selection of the spot where defaecation is to occur. Following defaecation, a stallion usually turns and smells the spot where it has taken place. After defaecation, in the case of both the stallion and the mare, the muscles of the perineum contract and the tail is lashed downwards several times.

While urinating the stallion and the gelding adopt a characteristic stance, the hind legs being abducted and extended so that the back becomes hollowed. Urination takes place with the penis retained in the sheath. Following urination, the stallion again smells around the area before walking away.

The mare, when urinating, does not show the same marked straddling posture as is shown by the stallion; nevertheless, the posture is similar in that the hind legs are abducted from each other. Following urination by the mare, the vulvar muscles contract. More elaborate patterns of urination are shown by brood mares with young foals and by mares in oestrus.

As already mentioned, horses typically show care in selecting areas for defaecation. They return again and again to the same patch. These patches can accumulate large quantities of faeces during a grazing season. Adult animals defaecate six to twelve times per day, depending on the nature of the feedstuffs eaten. Normally urination occurs less often during the day and horses have been noted to urinate as few as three times per day. Most urine is passed during rest periods in the hours of darkness.

## GROOMING

In spite of both written and verbal reports to the contrary, horses do groom each other. At pasture, pairs of horses may spend quite lengthy periods in mutual grooming (Fig. 3). This form of grooming

Fig. 3.   Mutual 'saddle-grooming' in between foals. (tracing)

is shown in all age groups, though the pairs which are formed by individuals are usually matched for age and size. In the normal grooming position, two horses face each other; and one extends its head past the side of the other's neck and nibbles vigorously over the latter's saddle region. While engaged in this nibbling action, the first animal is usually likewise being groomed by the second.

Horses also spend time grooming their own bodies, particularly around the hip and flank. This is effected by turning round, extending the head, and nibbling repeatedly at the skin in these regions. They may occasionally also groom their limbs in the same manner.

Rolling at pasture is probably also a form of grooming in the horse. Here a horse lies down in a normal fashion and then proceeds to kick itself over on to its back. Once in this position it rubs its back against the ground while keeping its feet up in the air. After several rubs it rolls on to its side again. In some circumstances it may roll on to its other side while, at other times, it rolls back on to the side from which the roll started. Another form of grooming by horses is to be seen when they vigorously scrub the roots of their tails and adjacent hindquarters against fixed objects such as trees or posts. While this behaviour is often taken to be a symptom of parasitism, it also should be realized that this habit may be practised by some horses which are not pathologically parasitized.

# SOCIAL PATTERNS

## *Social Behaviour*

Whilst being a typical herd species, horses also show a marked preference for certain individuals of their own species. Two horses encountering each other for the first time, show much more mutual exploratory behaviour than is seen in the other farm animal species. Exploratory behaviour at introduction involves an investigation of the other's head, body and hindquarters using the olfactory sense.

As with the other farm animals horses show a form of social order when they live in groups, and a social hierarchy becomes established within these groups. The older and larger animals are usually found to be high in the dominance order. Stallions do not necessarily dominate geldings or mares. A dominant individual often dictates the movement of the herd throughout the grazing area and will sometimes break up exchanges between other horses. Socially dominant horses are sometimes found to have more aggressive termperaments than the others. Horses running at pasture show special features of behaviour if the group contains a stallion and breeding mares. Stallions usually drive younger male animals to the perimeter of their groups, but will not show any aggressive attitudes towards them if they remain there. The stallion attempts to herd a group of brood mares together. The normal size of 'harem' amongst horses is about seven to eight mares. The colts tend to form a bachelor group, after splitting off from the herd at the age of about 1 to 2 years. Fillies may or may not join this group.

## Vocalization

It has been suggested that the horse makes three basic sounds: a neigh, a grunt and a high-pitched crying noise. These sounds vary in their degree of intensity and duration, and also show variations according to sex and age, and the particular stimulus which elicits them. There are also specific sounds which are variations of the three basic ones.

The neigh is the loudest noise emitted by the horse. It is often heard when a mare is separated from her foal or when a horse is

Fig. 4. A stallion trumpeting. Note the full nasal expansion. (tracing)

curious about events outside its range of vision, or when it is seeking to communicate with other horses. Three types of grunt can be distinguished: the most frequent just prior to feeding, the second emitted by stallions at the beginning of a sexual encounter and the third when the mare has cause to worry about her foal. The crying or squealing sound can vary in volume and is usually heard during aggressive encounters, i.e. as a part of threat behaviour, in fighting or in instances of aggressive sexual rejection.

An additional form of vocalization in the male is trumpeting (Fig. 4).

## Agonistic Behaviour

Agonistic behaviour embodies the behavioural activities of fight and flight and those of aggressive and passive behaviour; i.e.

Fig. 5.   Agonistic exchange between foals. (tracing)

agonistic behaviour includes all forms of behaviour by an animal
which is in conflict, physically or otherwise, with another animal.
   Horses are unpredictable in the way in which they display
agonistic behaviour. Under farming conditions, the response to
alarm or threat may be flight or attempted flight on the one hand
or attack on the other. Horses attack using their teeth and hind
feet. It is thought that aggressive acts in horses maintained in
isolation may be the result of excitement or habit. Many stockmen
and experienced horsemen hold the view that a tendency towards
aggressive behaviour in horses can be recognized in association
with certain physical features. They also hold that certain colours
in horses and certain characteristics of the head and the eyes
portray a temperament in which aggressive behaviour is a feature.
While it is difficult to refute opinions based on long experience by
association, it must also be recognized that such opinions may be
based on prejudice. It is certainly difficult to justify, on scientific
grounds, belief that a horse's temperament is predetermined by
certain morphological characteristics.

# SUPPLEMENTARY READING

HAFEZ, E. S. E., WILLIAMS, M. & WIERZBOWSKI, S. (1969) The behaviour of horses. In: *The Behaviour of Domestic Animals*, ed. E. S. E. Hafez, 2nd ed., chapter 12. London: Baillière, Tindall & Cassell.

NISHIKAWA, Y. (1959) *Studies on Reproduction in Horses.* Tokyo: Japan Racing Association.

NISHIKAWA, Y. & HAFEZ, E. S. E. (1969) Reproduction of horses. In: *Reproduction in Farm Animals*, ed. E. S. E. Hafez, 2nd ed., chapter 17. Philadelphia: Lea & Febiger.

PRAHOV, R. (1959) Inducing oestrus and accelerating ovulation in mares by reflex methods. *Nauč. Trud. naučno-izsled. Inst. Razvăd. Bol. izkustu. Osemen. Selskostop. Zivoth., 1,* 69–76. (*Anim. Breed. Abstr.* (1962) *30,* No. 800).

SCHNEIDER, K. M. (1930) Das Flehmen. *Zool. Gart., Leipzig, 4.* 183–198.

WIERZBOWSKI, S. (1959) The sexual reflexes of stallions. *Roczn. Naukro ln. B. 73,* 753–788 (*Anim. Breed. Abstr.* (1960) *28,* No. 500).

ZEEB, K. (1961) Der freie Herdensprung bei Pferden. *Wien. tierärztl. Mschr., 48,* 90–102.

# 5.

# Behaviour Patterns in Cattle

## INGESTION

### *Grazing and Feeding*

Unlike horses and sheep which have incisor teeth and therefore can bite grass, cattle have to rely for food intake on the high mobility of the tongue, which is used to encircle a patch of grass and then to draw it into the mouth, where the lower teeth and the tongue are used to sever the bound grass.

The nature of a cow's feeding accessories is such that it is virtually impossible for the animal to graze less than 1 cm from the ground. When grazing, the cow moves about chewing the grass or plant only two or three times whilst, at the same time, moving its head from one side to the other seeking the next patch of herbage to feed on. In this manner cattle graze mostly during the hours of daylight and cover, on average, about 4 km per day. The distance travelled increases if the weather is hot or wet or if there is an abundance of flies around. During the season of hot weather, more grazing may be done at night than during the day. In each 24-hour period, there are four main periods of high ingestive intake: (1) shortly prior to sunrise, (2) mid-morning, (3) early afternoon and (4) near dusk. Of these distinct periods, the hours prior to sunrise and around dusk appear to be the periods of longest and most continuous grazing. During other times of the day, cattle graze intermittently and idle, rest or ruminate. At such times selectivity is low; but prior to the periods of high intake, selectivity of pasture and food plants increases becoming very marked during the high intake phase. After a while grazing becomes intermittent again and the level of selectivity decreases.

Newborn calves do not graze until they are several days old and their first attempts are usually inefficient. But as the periods of suckling are reduced, grazing becomes more regular and calves become highly selective in their grazing intake.

The average time cattle spend grazing during the 24-hour period is 4 to 9 hours. The periods of rumination may also total 4 to 9 hours and the number of ruminating periods may be fifteen to twenty. The number of drinks taken per day is one to four, and the hours spent lying down are usually in the 9- to 12-hour range. These figures may vary in different respects between beef cattle and dairy cattle and in tropical and in free-ranging herds, but behaviour in domestic cattle is usually fairly stable and the figures given are reasonably accurate.

Cattle, like sheep, show evidence of conscious selective intake when grazing, and the same controversial theories of 'nutritional wisdom'—as to whether an individual animal is able to balance its metabolism with the correct amount of the various necessary constituents—have been propounded. Cattle show a particular tendency for selection of certain plants and grasses. Their degree of selectivity can be high and they may prefer plants of a particular species, and even those species only at a certain stage of growth. The effects of this selectivity can be seen in the condition of a pasture area inhabited by cattle. The growth on the grazing area is erratic; while some places may have thick growths of herbage, others are thin and patchy indicating the existence of a favourite food. Cattle usually avoid plants which have been contaminated by excreta or have a hairy or unpleasant appearance. They may select different types of grass by smell, but the stimulus of taste is thought to be the main factor in deciding selectivity when grazing. The stimuli of sight and smell do both influence the pattern of the grazing behaviour of cattle, but they play only a minor part in food selection. Calves are able to consume a fairly large quantity of feedstuffs which contain an acid ingredient, but cattle prefer glucose to acid foodstuffs and to salty or sour substances.

With regard to their ability to maintain correctly a balance of nutrients in their systems, it has certainly been found that some cattle are able to correct a sodium deficiency; but, as with sheep, experiments have not been extensive or conclusive enough to warrant any singular statement on the subject.

Cattle and sheep being ruminants can utilize more fibrous foodstuffs and require greater bulk. In addition cattle show more variety in ingestive behaviour when grazing extensively. In general, large animals eat more quickly than small ones, and alfalfa requires more chewing before ingestion than ground corn which, in its turn, requires more chewing than shelled corn. The time taken to consume food varies according to its volume, the concentrates which may be in it, whether it is wet or dry, and the way a particular food has been processed before giving it to the animals. In dairy cattle a lot of eating takes place shortly after milking. Given a choice between silage and hay, milking cows will spend more time at the silage, often two-thirds of the total eating time, while spending the remaining one-third at hay. In a study of food choice, it was found that green fodders and roots were preferred to protein while cereal chaff was preferred to straw.

In the main, the behaviour pattern of cattle in temperate climates is fairly regular and the individuals characteristically behave as a group, idling, resting, ruminating or grazing at the same time. Cattle have, however, been known suddenly to change their preferences, when supplied with food in a closed area over a long period of time.

## *Rumination*

Following ingestion comes rumination. Rumination allows cattle to regurgitate, masticate and then swallow food which they have previously ingested into the rumen. Thus animals can continue their digestive activities at leisure, when away from a preferred

Fig. 6. A cow chewing cud while resting on her sternum—a posture which facilitates rumination by increasing stomach pressure. (tracing)

grazing area or sheltering during bad weather. Usually cattle prefer to lie down during rumination although in bad weather, e.g. heavy rain, they may prefer to stand or walk about slowly. Rumination does occur in young calves, but only takes up a proportion of daily time comparable to that in adults after about 6 to 8 months of age. During the 24-hour cycle, rumination takes place about fifteen to twenty times, but the duration of each period may differ vastly; it may last only 2 minutes or so or it may continue up to 1 hour or even more at one stretch. The peak period for rumination is shortly after nightfall; thereafter, it steadily declines until shortly before dawn when grazing begins. Times may differ, however, according to diet; cattle are able to regurgitate, remasticate and reswallow long hay more quickly than ground hay or concentrates. The relation between the time spent grazing and the time spent ruminating varies depending on the season and the abundance and quality of the herbage provided, along with the area available to the cows and the size of the herd. The time spent ruminating amounts, on average, to three-quarters of the time spent grazing. Good quality herbage nearly always shortens the time spent ruminating, while herbage which is rough increases the number and length of ruminating periods. In the spring and autumn the time spent grazing almost totally eclipses the periods of rumination, but in the summer they are almost equal.

The factors which may disturb or cause the cessation of rumination are various. During oestrus ruminating nearly always falls away, but it does not stop altogether. Any incident which gives rise to pain, hunger, maternal anxiety or illness affects ruminating activities. The periods pre- and post-parturition are not conducive to rumination and it may decline to a low level. Some animal scientists hold the view that the longer rumination is interrupted or delayed, the more difficult it becomes for the animal to resume this activity.

## Drinking

This activity refers to the total consumption of water, including that water which is often contained in the animal feed. Cattle usually drink one to four times a day in temperate climates; they do so more often in hot weather and when there is a high proportion of concentrates in their food.

Cattle drink using their muzzles. The tongue, unlike at grazing or feeding, plays little part in the process and the nostrils are kept above the surface of the water. Cattle usually drink in the forenoon, early afternoon and evening but rarely at night or at dawn. More drinking is done on old pastures than in nutritious grazing areas. Cattle given an abundance of feedingstuff—a situation which may occur during housing—tend to consume more water than they would normally. In addition to hot weather and an abundance of various types of feedstuffs, milking also induces cows to drink. Thus soon after milking and especially after the evening milking, cattle drink water whenever possible. It may be significant that milk is 88% water.

Several other factors alter or discourage drinking activities. The water intake increases during late pregnancy and lactation, and the intake varies according to the ambience of the temperature, breed, age, body-size, intake of pasture and the level of nutrient and salt in the food provided. European breeds of cattle drink more than tropical breeds whether during temperate or very hot weather, and cattle fed on foodstuffs with a high level of protein drink much more than those on a lower protein supplement. The amount of water consumed by pregnant heifers has been calculated to be 28 to 32 kg per day while the average daily intake of water by adults is about 14 kg.

# ELIMINATION

During the 24-hour daily cycle cattle normally urinate about nine times and defaecate twelve to eighteen times. The number of times cattle engage in eliminative behaviour and the volume that is expelled, however, varies with the nature and quantity of food ingested, the ambience of the temperature and the individual animal itself. Holstein cattle may expel 40 kg of faeces in the 24-hour cycle while Jerseys are found to defaecate some 28 kg under the same conditions.

Although the eliminative behaviour of cattle is neither specifically regulated in the frequency of its occurrence nor consciously directed at a certain area, large amounts of faeces are often placed closely together. At night and during bad weather cattle tend to bunch, and this would appear to be the only reason for the close deposition of faeces. The animals pay little attention to the faeces, often walking and lying amongst the excreta. There is evidence that in some dairy cows allelomimetic behaviour is engendered and when one animal defaecates or urinates others may commence to do likewise.

The normal defaecation stance for both male and female animals is one in which the tail is flexed away from the posterior region, the back arched and the hind legs placed forward and apart. The posture assumed is such that there is the least possible risk of incurring contamination. This attitude towards hygiene is also seen in calves which in fact take more care than adults to expel the faeces well away from the body. Unlike the female, the male bovine animal is able to walk while urinating and only displays a slight parting of the legs while doing so. The posture assumed by the female while urinating is very much the same as that employed while defaecating, and the urine is expelled more forcefully by the female than the male. The amount of urine passed is usually between 10 and 15 kg for the 24-hour period.

# SOCIAL PATTERNS

## *Agonistic Behaviour*

When one bovine makes a passive approach towards another of the same species, a mild threat by the latter may often be enough to discourage the approaching animal from engaging in physical contact. If, however, the attacked animal is slow to react it may be butted, often from the rear. The nature of the up-swinging motion of the butt may cause serious injury to a bull or cow, particularly if the attacking animal has horns.

An active approach on the other hand, by one animal towards another, is seen when the former makes a deliberate threat. If the latter animal resents this approach, its resentment is indicated by the lowering of its head as in aggressive behaviour, but the animal's forehead is positioned nearly parallel to the ground with its neck extended. However, if the animal being threatened in its turn displays threatening behaviour, fighting ensues. In some cases the two opponents stand a few metres apart with their heads lowered, hind legs drawn forward, eyes on each other and with their horns

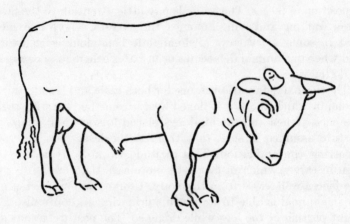

Fig. 7. The 'fight or flight' display in the bull. (tracing)

directed in the same manner. The threat posture of females is similar to the fight or flight posture of males. Other forms of threat behaviour are seen when an animal paws at the ground, rubs its head and neck on the ground and also its horns (where these are present).

When fighting ensues, the animals fight with their heads and horns and try to butt each others' flanks. If one animal manoeuvres itself into a position whereby it can butt the flank of the other, the second animal turns round to defend itself and attempts a similar attack. Fighting does not normally last longer than a few minutes, but in cases where the animals are equally matched the 'clinch' move may be employed. This is a move where the animal being attacked from the side, turns itself parallel to the other and pushes its head and horns into the region of the other's udder. This often results in a temporary cessation of fighting which may last for several minutes before action is resumed. When one animal submits it turns and runs from the other which may assert its dominance by chasing after it for a few metres. If neither animal submits, fighting may continue until both opponents suffer from physical exhaustion.

Fighting between females, apart from causing physical injury, can result in a reduction of milk-yield since the inhibited subjects may not feed properly in a restricted area. It is best to keep the new cows in an adjacent field to that of the main herd at first, before introducing the animals one by one to the other members, thus allowing the individuals to become used to each other. Even then fighting may occur as the new animals may struggle to attain positions in the social and domination hierarchy of the whole herd.

## Social Hierarchy

One of the most important patterns of behaviour in the range of group interactions is that of the social hierarchy or dominance order in a group of animals which may spend a long time living together. This is specially notable between cattle. When a social hierarchy is set up in a herd of cattle, it will usually last a very long time although minor adjustments to an individual's social rank are inevitable. The existence of a solid social hierarchy is important for the welfare of a herd.

The way in which this order is evolved often varies from breed to breed. Chest girth may sometimes be enough to assert one animal's dominance over another while, on the other hand, height at the withers or total weight may be the deciding factor. It has been found in closed herds that seniority, i.e. age, often influences the social order. It is worth noting that in dairy herds where seniority defines social rank, no newcomers have been introduced into the herd; the only new animals being the ones that are born within the herd. In large open herds, where animals may encounter each other for the first time at any age, the order is usually based on strength and weight. It has been stated after observations that in general Ayrshires dominate Jerseys and that Angus dominate Shorthorns who in their turn dominate Herefords. Often in these cases, the assertion of one animal's domination over another is not based on size, strength or seniority but on the hereditary characteristics of the members of the different breeds.

In cattle varying types of social hierarchy can be seen. There is the *linear hierarchy* in which one animal dominates another, which dominates a third, the hierarchy continuing in this manner through the entire herd; the last animal being dominated by all the others. This social order is not seen markedly in large herds and usually only exists within quite small herds in which the animals have been living together over a long period of time.

The *linear-tending hierarchies* are slightly more complex and occur more frequently. These hierarchies have a normal linear dominance order, except in one sense. At the top there is a situation where one animal dominates all the others, except for one, which in turn is dominated by a third animal which is above all the rest except for the first. Thus there is a triangle at the top of the linear-tending hierarchy where each animal dominates all but one. In linear-tending situations, this triangle may occur in the middle of the social order or at its bottom.

Another social order is the *complex hierarchy* where several animals may dominate a certain number in the group, while being themselves dominated by others, which are dominated by several of the initial animals.

Social hierarchies often change as the young males in a mixed group begin to challenge the females in the group. When they are about 18 months old, they come to dominate all the females and join the other adult males which also dominate the females. Fierce fighting is not specifically required to form the hierarchy, even when a new animal has been introduced. Often a threat posture or a movement of the head is enough to determine one animal's dominance over another (Fig. 8A), and there is evidence that the main structure of the order is based on visual factors. Even in breeds with spectacular horn development such as the Steppes cattle (Fig. 8B) these exchanges are purely formal.

It has often been assumed that the members of the herd which are leaders, by the way they influence the movement of the others, are the most dominant animals in the group; but this is not invariably the case. In a free-moving herd, the animals which occupy the middle region of the dominance order are usually the ones which lead. They are often followed by animals which, although they are at the top of the dominance order, are content to occupy the middle of the moving group while the animals most dominated remain at the rear. When cattle are put in a position where they are required to move, for example, into a milking parlour, the order in which they do so is fairly constant, but seems to bear no relation to the weight, size or age of the animals (except for the fact that pregnant cows are usually found at the rear of any group forcibly being moved). While grazing, one or two animals may lead the rest moving in a particular direction but if these two leaders separate and the herd follows the movement of one leader then the other is forced to concede and to return, taking

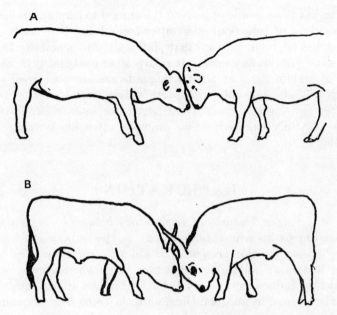

Fig. 8. (A) Head to head challenge in the determination of social rank (peak-order) in cattle. Note the token nature of the exchange. (B) Head to head pushing contest between two young bulls of Steppe breed. In this exchange the potentially lethal horns possessed by this breed are not brought into decisive use. (tracings)

up the general direction of the herd. Usually the two leaders are able to adjust to each other and to avoid splitting up the herd.

It thus appears that there are three social orders in a group of cattle: the social or dominance hierarchy, the order in forced movement and the leader–follower structure.

## Play

The characteristic aspects of behaviour displayed in play activities by cattle are prancing, kicking, pawing, snorting, vocalizing and head-shaking. These are seen particularly in young calves, although adults do occasionally indulge in playful activities. It has been said that play behaviour provides the participating animal with its own method of release of energy drive and, with regard to the young, has the purpose of helping the animal to acquire the essential motives of behaviour encountered in adults. Conversely, the theory has been put forward that play is simply an activity for its own sake without any underlying purpose or goal and that, in the case of playful fighting, the participants are not concerned with which will win, but only with participation in the activity itself. Playful fighting is distinct from aggressive interactions in that while playfully engaged, either animal's attention is easily distracted.

# EXPLORATION

One of the main features of exploratory behaviour is that it is engaged in by an animal only as long as the emotions of fear or apprehension are not present. The animal's curiosity is aroused when it sees an unfamiliar object or hears an unknown noise. What may induce exploratory behaviour in one animal may very often be ignored by another. Older animals, being more acquainted with the objects and sounds of their environment, are less curious and exploratory behaviour is therefore a character of young animals. When curiosity is first aroused the animal assumes a posture similar to that of surrender or submissiveness, but with nostrils quivering and sniffing. The size and nature of the object, in which the animal has become interested, determines the speed of approach. It sniffs the object and may lick or even, if the object is malleable enough, chew and swallow it. This kind of exploratory behaviour is often induced by the sight of familiar objects in unfamiliar surroundings or vice versa. It is stressed however that the animal's curiosity is rarely followed through if it has any cause for fear or apprehension.

# SLEEPING AND RESTING

It has been observed that there exists no concrete evidence that adult cattle do in fact experience a state of sleep. Apparently if they do, it is in very short, broken periods within each 24-hour diurnal and nocturnal period and when in a resting position. Cattle rest for about 9 to 12 hours of the 24-hour period and often favour lying on one side rather than the other. The forelimbs are curled under the body and one hind leg is tucked forward underneath with the other one stretched out in front of the body. They will occasionally lie fully on their sides, but do so only for very short periods and hold their heads in a level erect position to facilitate swallowing and expulsion of gases from the rumen. Although adult cattle do take up the sleeping position seen in calves, with their heads resting in towards the flanks, this is more rarely and spasmodically seen, and it is uncertain whether this is a resting or a sleeping position in adults.

# GROOMING

Cattle lick and thereby clean every part of their bodies that they can reach. To groom inaccessible parts they often make use of trees and fences, and by using their tails they keep off flies and brush their skins. The value of grooming is seen in that it helps to remove mud, faeces, urine and parasites, and thus greatly reduces the risk of disease. It has been estimated that calves spend up to 52 minutes a day grooming themselves by scratching and licking. Adult cattle may lick themselves on 152 occasions during a day and scratch twenty-eight times a day.

When one animal grooms another, it is commonly found the one engaged in cleaning is slightly below the other in the social order (though normally within three positions). In large mixed

Fig. 9. Grooming between two heifers. The animal being groomed has turned the side of its neck in the direction of the groomer. (tracing)

herds, adult males will groom each other more often than younger animals or females. Their grooming is applied mostly around the area of the head and neck. It has been suggested that one animal grooms another to enjoy the salt properties of the outer skin layers, but it could also be the behaviour of a subordinate creature appeasing its superior.

## SUPPLEMENTARY READING

BROWNLEE, A. (1954) Play in domestic cattle in Britain: an analysis of its nature. *Br. vet. J., 110*, 48–68.

BROWNLEE, A. (1957) Higher nervous activity in domestic cattle. *Br. vet. J., 113*, 407–416.

HAFEZ, E. S. E. & SCHEIN, M. W. (1969) The behaviour of cattle. In: *The Behaviour of Domestic Animals*, ed. E. S. E. Hafez, 2nd ed., chapter 9. London: Baillière, Tindall & Cassell.

SCHEIN, M. W. & FOHRMAN, M. W. (1955) Social dominance relationships in a herd of dairy cattle. *Br. J. Anim. Behav., 3*, 45–55.

SCHLOETH, R. (1958) Cycle annuel et comportment social du tanreau de Camargue. *Mammalia, 22*, 121.

TRIBE, D. E. (1955) The behaviour of grazing animals. In: *Progress in the Physiology of Farm Animals*, ed. J. Hammond, vol. 2, p. 585. London: Butterworths.

WHITEHEAD, G. K. (1953) *The Ancient White Cattle of Britain and their Descendants*. London: Faber & Faber.

# 6.
# Behaviour Patterns in Sheep

## DAILY CYCLE OF BEHAVIOUR

The day-to-day pattern of feeding, rumination and allelomimetic behaviour in sheep depends largely for its variability on seasonal factors, breed of sheep, geographical situation of available land and the nutritional and chemical qualities of the grazing pasture.

### *Locomotion*

In temperate conditions, a flock will set out into the pasture, moving together and then fanning out. However, although they may move some distance from each other, sheep often form sub-groups within the main flock and continue to exist as a concerted group, following a regular pattern of movement around the grazing land.

The distance travelled by sheep while grazing is affected both by the immediate environment of the flock and by genetic differences affecting the behaviour of different breeds in adapting to the particular habitats in which they were reared. Thus Cheviot breed sheep travel further than those of the Romney Marsh breed when both subspecies are kept in hilly country but only a little further when both graze on flat areas. Ewes of Hampshire breed travel less than those of Columbia or Rombouillet breeds. The distance covered by sheep, during temperate conditions, usually remains constant. The only major alteration to this behaviour occurs shortly before the breeding season when movement, particularly amongst the rams, becomes less regulated. Generally sheep travel about 8 to 16 km per day, although any increase in the duration of grazing time results in a corresponding increase in distance travelled. Likewise, any increase in available feeding space has a similar effect. These effects, however, are usually temporary and cause no major alterations to the overall behaviour pattern of the flock.

## Social Patterns

An important feature of behaviour in sheep is their marked allelomimetic activity and well developed practice of social co-existence. In a comparative study of two separate flocks of sheep kept on the same grazing pasture for several days and nights, there was found to be no difference in the start or finish of the major grazing periods. Likewise, it was noticeable that no single animal was the instigator of any grazing or resting period. Although individual sheep rested or grazed at different times than the main flocks, the presence of any dominating animal which influenced the pattern of behaviour of the combined flocks was not noted.

In the main, sheep tend to form groups which remain in a particular area. In hilly country sheep 'bed down' on the hills themselves and move to the hillier areas, if possible, during winter. In hot weather they seek out the shade of bushes and trees, and areas close to water. Although these home ranges are specific in the areas covered, neighbouring sheep may share common ground and small numbers of sheep often settle down along a boundary, or in a corner of a small grazing area common to another small group from an adjacent pasture. Although rams also have specific areas in which they tend to remain, their boundaries are less clearly defined than those of ewes, and they may change their locale just prior to the breeding season.

In the mating season, rams emit a hoarse 'baaing' sound when approaching ewes. *Vocalization* also plays an important part in the maintenance of communication between members of the flock. If a mother is separated from her young she will 'baa' until they are brought together and the young do the same. Even adult members of the flock, which become disengaged from the others 'baa' and with increased vocalization become more animated in attempts to locate the main flock. Increased vocalization has been shown to be accompanied by increased mobility. However, while in a young lamb separated from its dam, or an adult sheep separated from the main flock, vocalization is fairly intense initially, it declines after about 4 hours of continuous separation.

# SEASONAL CYCLE OF BEHAVIOUR

The general behaviour patterns of sheep which have been described are aspects of behaviour which occur, commonly, from day to day and are not affected by season changes. There are, however, several important types of behaviour which occur during a particular season, often associated with breeding or sexual behaviour. During the summer, if it is very hot, sheep may graze more at night than during the day. Conversely, in winter they do more grazing in the hours of daylight. In autumn there is a large increase in sexual behaviour and consequently fighting or agonistic behaviour, between the rams. Rams engage in running towards one another and butting; they may buffet each other with their shoulders, engage in bunching and running activities, or emit snorting sounds and paw the earth with their forefeet. This may partly explain the movement of rams, from one restricted area to another, which occurs in autumn and also the unsettled nature of ram groupings with regard to the members of the group.

# INGESTION

In the main, the general features of ingestive behaviour of sheep are those common to all the farm animals. There are periods of movement and eating as well as of drinking, idling and lying down and ruminating, interspersed with periods of intensive ingestive activity. Some animals eat less than others, others spend more time lying down, but there are particular features of behaviour which typify the sheep.

## *Grazing, Feeding and Drinking*

Sheep do not graze continuously. They have specific stages, during the 24-hour daily cycle, when ingestive intake is very high and others when grazing is punctuated by ruminating, resting and idling. The ruminating behaviour of sheep varies from breed to breed. Some breeds prefer to remain in a particular part of the available grazing space where the nutritional quality of the grass and plants may be very high. Other breeds prefer to split up into groups throughout the area, occupying particular spots. Breeds, in which ruminating behaviour is more marked and which prefer to move about the available space, may find that some parts of the land do not provide appropriate herbage. These animals continue to move about, even though some of the available food may not be to their liking.

The longest and also the most intensive periods of grazing take place in the early morning and from late afternoon to dusk. The number of grazing periods over each 24-hour cycle averages four to seven times, and the total grazing time usually amounts to about 10 hours. Although adult sheep usually eat more than do lambs, the pattern of their ingestive intake is less uniform, and in fact some may eat less than the lambs, while others consume a comparatively large quantity of food and water. The number of rumination periods may amount to fifteen during the 24-hour cycle. Although the total time of rumination may be from 8 to 10 hours, the length of each period may differ vastly; from 1 minute to anything up to 2 hours. The adult intake of water is from 3 to 6 litres, and the number of urinations and defaecations total approximately 9 to 13 and 6 to 8 respectively. The average grazing intake of an individual sheep may differ greatly from that of the main flock, and the amount ingested may also be affected by the presence of lambs. It is widely recognized that sheep prefer certain plants and grasses to others, and of the plants that they prefer some may prove more palatable to the animal than others. The fertility of the soil, the use or non-use of fertilizers, the geographical situation of the grazing land and the nature of the climate, all affect the grazing behaviour of the flock.

In cases of restriction sheep nibble the grass very close to the ground and faeces are often deposited where there is good quality grazing. Sheep do not normally consume plants or grass which have been contaminated by faeces, but when circumstances prevail, the sheep do consume the good herbage in spite of contamination.

The feeding and drinking habits of sheep are in some ways affected by ambient temperature, quality of grain and specific breed. It is known that, as the temperature drops, a sheep's food intake correspondingly increases; but if it becomes very cold the animal's appetite becomes inhibited and the intake declines. Sheep are known to have developed senses of smell, taste and visual recognition of food, but their intake is almost unaffected when they are made to eat without the aid of vision. They do not often however eat plants which are hairy or greasy.

It has been suggested that sheep are able to select what items of food they eat, and thereby correct any nutritional deficiencies or excesses. Certainly, sheep with definite nutritional deficiencies have been known to correct their nutritional balance by consuming plants and grains which will do so. Sheep generally accept food of a balanced quality rather than food of a more erratic composition. Findings in this field have not been uniform, however, and many sheep are found to persist in eating a particular crop or plant, which further upsets an already unbalanced nutritional condition.

Nevertheless, one evident aspect of the feeding activities of sheep is that they are fairly adaptable regarding the plants, grass and crops which are made available to them. They do tend to develop particular likings for certain crops and may even prefer one type of food, which is exactly the same in content as another but prepared differently. They are however also able to adapt themselves to a particular species of grass or plant if there are no other nutrients to be found and, eventually, the disliked food plant apparently becomes palatable. The stage in its development and its body weight have an effect on a sheep's food intake, more so than adjustments to sensory faculties. On average sheep consume food equivalent to 2·5% of their bodyweight per day.

Possibly as a result of allelomimetic behaviour, sheep often form specific paths to water sources, and follow a recognized route rather than a direct one across grazing land, regardless of the time factor involved. They also generally tend to frequent a particular watering place. As with feeding, the amount of water consumed varies according to breed, quality of pasture and weather conditions. Vocal activities and seasonal changes likewise influence the amount of water consumed.

## Rumination

Cud-chewing periods number about eight per 24-hours and in this respect are not very different from the ruminating periods of cattle. Rumination in sheep, however, occurs at irregular intervals throughout the night and day and, although there may be a higher frequency of rumination early in the morning and fairly regular rumination in mid-afternoon, these tendencies are not marked and cannot be said to be characteristic of all breeds of sheep. It has not yet been ascertained fully exactly what induces the onset and cessation of rumination, but neural stimuli would seem to be involved. The consumption of chopped hay apparently invokes more frequent rumination than long hay and sheep, when fed small quantities of food at regular intervals instead of receiving one large feed, show a marked increase in rumination and regurgitation.

## *Suckling*

One of the most noticeable behavioural aspects of a sheep in relation to newborn is the strong maternal relationship which often develops. A dam nearly always vigorously rejects any attempts by other lambs to engage in sucking and will look after her own young exclusively.

Most newborn lambs are able to stand within the first half hour following birth, and nearly all are able to stand within the first 2 hours. The lamb's first attempts to suck are usually unsuccessful; it often seeks out the teat by nosing between the forelegs of the dam, or any nearby object which the lamb may feel has maternal properties. If, at this point, the newborn fails to find the teat or is prevented from doing so by the behaviour of the mother, its drive to suck may become inhibited.

Within about 1 hour of birth approximately 60% of the newborn have begun to suck and, in normal cases, nearly all the lambs have sought out the udder within the first 2 hours. Once the newborn is able to stand, it sucks and nibbles at any object which is at hand; this is usually the coat of the dam. While the dam is removing the placenta from the lamb, the latter finds its way to the region of the teats and udder. Sometimes the lamb is prevented from undertaking suckling by the diligent efforts of the mother to remove the placenta. If the udder is too large, the newborn may find the teat difficult to grasp. However, once the newborn can facilitate milk let-down by pushing the teat upwards into the udder with its mouth, progress in locating the teat again and sucking, becomes very rapid. In the first week following birth, lambs suck very frequently, sometimes on sixty to seventy occasions during the 24-hour period. The duration of suckling at this time is usually from 1 to 3 minutes, but later on the young are seldom allowed by the dam to suck for periods of over 20 seconds.

Single lambs do not usually favour one teat over another. In the case of twins though, each lamb does develop a preference for one particular teat, but this may change where the other twin objects. In cases where one of the twins is removed after a period, the remaining lamb begins to suck from the other teat too. Sometimes the dam facilitates suckling by lifting her hind leg on the side at which the newborn is attempting to suck. One aspect of behaviour characteristic of the newborn lamb is the vigorous wagging of its tail when engaged in suckling (see Fig. 47, p. 154). It has been postulated that this is a mechanism which entices the dam to smell the anal region and so recognize her young, for some dams do not discourage the approach of another newborn if it is similar in appearance to her own.

# ELIMINATION

There appears to be no recognizable pattern of defaecation in sheep. Urination often occurs when animals are disturbed.

# SUPPLEMENTARY READING

BANKS, E. M. (1964) Some aspects of sexual behaviour in domestic sheep, *Ovis aries. Behaviour*, 23, 249–279.

GEIST, V. (1971) *Mountain Sheep*. Chicago and London: University of Chicago Press.

GOODWIN, D. H. (1971) *The Production and Management of Sheep*. London: Hutchinson Educational.

HAFEZ, E. S. E. et al. (1969) The behaviour of sheep and goats. In: *The Behaviour of Domestic Animals*, ed. E. S. E. Hafez, 2nd ed., chapter 10. London: Baillière, Tindall & Cassell.

# 7.
# Behaviour Patterns in Pigs

## LOCOMOTION AND EXPLORATION

While young pigs are nimble and able to run about the mature pig, with its relatively massive trunk, is physically ill-equipped for movement at speed. Well grown pigs therefore only run distances of a few metres. They are, however, able to trot at a reasonable speed over long distances.

Pigs have long periods of inactivity each day. During these periods they typically rest in huddled groups. Various studies have shown that pigs are more active during the night hours. This appears to be so particularly in the case of sows in oestrus.

Much of the general activity of pigs appears to stem from their exploratory behaviour. They show a very well developed exploratory drive, most of which is directed at objects at floor level which are investigated by smelling, nibbling and rooting. Such actions may have a destructive effect on objects, where these are subject to continuous investigation by a group of pigs, which are severely restricted in their movements. This is apparently the underlying cause of the vice of tail-biting. The tendency to over-investigate specific items in their environment can be controlled to a degree by providing additional objects for investigation and some pig breeders, aware of this fact, provide growing pigs with objects to be used as toys. These include motor tyres and chains suspended from the ceiling. The provision of straw bedding also provides an alternative outlet for the investigatory activities of pigs.

## INGESTION

The ingestive behaviour of pigs is evidently closely linked with their exploratory drive. Out of doors the exploration of territory largely involves rooting activities. Rooting is certainly the salient feature of ingestive behaviour in pigs. Even when pigs are fed with finely ground foodstuffs they continue to show rooting activities. The snout of the pig is a highly developed sense organ and olfaction plays a large part in the determination of behaviour, not least of all in feeding activities. Pigs are omnivorous and, at free range, they eat a variety of vegetable materials. They may also eat some animals such as earthworms. Under modern systems of husbandry, however, it is usual for pigs to be fed on compounded feedstuffs. Pigs consume a sufficient quantity of food of this type for 24 hours, in 20 minutes of each day. When provided with this food in feed-hoppers the time spent each day on feeding may be somewhat longer.

The quantity of food that pigs consume is marginally affected by the palatability of the feedstuff. They appear to prefer feedstuffs with some sugar content. Preference is also shown for other constituents such as fishmeal, yeast, wheat and soya bean. Substances which reduce the intake of food include salt, fat, meatmeal and cellulose. As a general rule, pigs appear to eat wet foodstuffs more readily than dry ones, though much depends upon palatability. Under management conditions where pigs are handfed they typically show hunger when feeding time approaches, and it is evident that the temporal arrangement of their feeding activities is very well defined. Community feeding has various effects on behaviour; feeding behaviour is evidently stimulated by the sight of other pigs feeding. Pigs in groups are found to consume more food than pigs kept individually. Well grown animals kept in pens in groups of 6 to 8 should, therefore, be given enough feeding trough space to consume their own ration of food, without adjacent competitors being able to poach off them. It is estimated that pigs of approximately 90 kg live weight should have a minimum trough space of 35 cm each. For pig groups of this size, fed by a system of self-feeding hoppers, it has been estimated that one self-feeder is required for every five animals. Even when the hoppers are well filled, if these are too few, the pigs will not be able to avoid competition in obtaining their full daily quota of food.

In all animals appetite can have a genetic basis; this is certainly true of pigs and some breeds have greater hunger drives than others. It has also been noted that certain families of pigs have stronger feeding drives than others and that pigs from these families are usually faster growing. The selection of highly productive pigs, in many cases, involves very little more than selecting those genes which are basic to the feeding drive.

Feeding drives are often keen amongst breeding sows. These animals are regaining bodyweight which was lost during the preceding lactation and, for this reason, there is more competition amongst them than others during feeding time. The introduction of individual feeding stalls for sows has been a great help in dealing with this situation. The stalls operate best when sows are allowed access to a communal exercising area between feeds.

Self-feeding pigs randomly space their eating and drinking periods throughout the day. Of the two, eating is the preferred activity. Pigs quickly learn to drink from mechanical devices which supply water when some plate or button is pressed. Water drinking is influenced both by animal size and environmental conditions. Under normal conditions of management, full grown pigs consume approximately 8 kg water daily. Pregnant sows may drink more water than this; their consumption usually being in excess of 9 kg per day.

# ELIMINATION

Elimination does not take place at random in the pen; specific sites are chosen by pigs for defaecation and urination. In spite of a reputation to the contrary, pigs are extremely clean in their habits if the system of husbandry imposed upon them gives them the opportunity to express their normal behaviour patterns. Pig premises which are appropriately designed to create dunging areas are usually properly used by pigs. Pigs apparently have a keen sense of territory and, even in the most limited quarters, they reserve an area for sleeping accommodation and an area for excretion. This sleeping area is kept as clean and dry as is possible. Under conditions of crowding, it is sometimes difficult for groups of pigs to maintain organized eliminative behaviour. When growing pigs are allocated less than $1 m^2$ of floor area each, their eliminative behaviour becomes disorganized and uncontrolled. Much of a pig's eliminative behaviour is learned during infancy from mature animals, and if the behaviour patterns are not acquired by learning at an early age they may not be acquired at all. Such pigs, in their turn, are unable to pass on learned behaviour of this type. These pigs are usually observed to be contaminated with their own excreta, and their presence in large proportions in a pig herd is a reflection on the system of management.

Urination apart from its eliminative function is also useful in other contexts. When penned pigs are exposed to high ambient temperatures and their normal behavioural methods of controlling hyperthermia cannot operate, it is common for them to urinate in a part of the pen and thereafter to wallow in this urine. The passing of small quantities of urine is observed in both sexes during the precoital period.

The patterns of eliminative behaviour whilst being learned from each other are also influenced by the location of food and water sources. It is commonly found that pigs excrete close to the source of their drinking water.

## THERMOREGULATION

Because of their morphological characteristics pigs are ill-suited to extremes of ambient temperature. They receive poor body insulation from their sparse covering of hair. They have very little loose skin from which to radiate excessive body heat and their sweat glands are confined to their snouts. In spite of these physical

Fig. 10.   Huddling in piglets showing parallel and opposite, and overlaying
          arrangements. (tracing)

inadequacies, pigs are able to adjust to temperature extremes through specific thermoregulatory behaviour.

The ability of newborn piglets to adapt to their environmental temperature is very limited as they are prone to rapidly losing body heat. The behavioural mechanism for dealing with this problem is huddling. From the time of birth, young piglets display huddling behaviour (Fig. 10) as an organized attitude for most of the day. During huddling they lie parallel to each other, often with head and tail ends alternating along the row. Whilst lying closely together side by side, they usually have their limbs tucked underneath them. When a group is large, some of the piglets in the middle may overlie others. The result of this huddling behaviour is that the quantity of heat lost by the piglets is much less than would be lost otherwise. Although huddling behaviour is characteristically shown in the litter early in life, it is nevertheless a behavioural pattern which is retained by groups of piglets, into adult life, as a means of conserving body heat.

Through their physical characteristics pigs, more so than any other farm animals, are susceptible to heat stress. In the presence of a high ambient temperature, they are singularly ill-equipped physically to radiate heat. Given access to water, they engage in wallowing activities (Fig. 11) during which they wet all the ventral

Fig. 11. A sow wallowing. (tracing)

areas of the body and give up excessive body heat by conduction. Under field conditions in warm weather pigs create mud-wallows. Wallowing in mud, in addition to permitting heat to be conducted from the body, also causes a reduction in body temperature by radiation; this allows pigs to forage extensively in excessive ambient temperatures.

Studies on the development of heat stress in pigs show that they

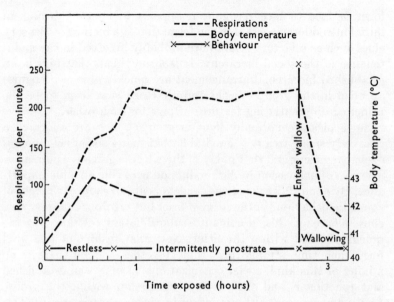

Fig. 12. Behaviour in relation to incipient heat stress in a pig. Wallowing is seen to control the syndrome.

can develop hyperthermia within a very short space of time; but, providing that it is possible for the body surface to be wetted, hyperthermia can be controlled to the point where animal health and comfort are not impaired. Close studies have been made on the effect of wallowing on a rapidly developing state of hyperthermia in sows in the tropics. In some instances it was noted that actual heat stress was brought under control by the pigs' voluntary wallowing activities (Fig. 12).

## SOCIAL AND AGONISTIC BEHAVIOUR

The social organization of groups of pigs is known to depend upon the establishment of a social hierarchy. For the social hierarchy to function properly, the size of a group and the space allocated to it are important. It is also necessary for the members of the group to be capable of prompt recognition of each other. In pigs, it is still uncertain how the mechanics of recognition operate, though it is evident that different types of recognition exist. A form of face to face recognition appears to operate during an initial introductory period in the formation of a hierarchy. Sensory clues such as olfactory stimuli are probably involved in the maintenance of the social hierarchy. It is also evident that pigs in an established hierarchial arrangement are quickly able to recognize an alien in the group. Visual and olfactory cues seem to be the principal differentiating features of pigs for each other.

Since pigs are normally kept in groups which are allocated a relatively small area it is inevitable that many social behavioural exchanges occur and that many of these have aggressive outcomes. The role of aggression in pig production is of considerable importance. By about 2 weeks of age, piglets begin to show exchanges of agonistic behaviour in the form of brief but vigorous fighting. As a consequence of this, dominance–subordination relationships are quickly formed within the litter. New relationships of this kind form each time strange pigs come together. Where there is no mixing of this kind, social organizations become well established and functional, and they reduce aggression within the group. Limited aggression within a group of pigs conserves energy. This in turn reflects in production. Dominance in the hierarchy ensures that an individual is able to carry out chosen behaviour. When competition for food or space increases, aggressive behaviour within the group increases. The buildup of aggressive behaviour leads to a weakening of the social hierarchy and, in due course, may cause it to break down completely. Some forms of abnormal behaviour in pigs are likely to be associated with pathological increases in aggressive behaviour resulting from instability in the social hierarchy. The stocking density in groups of pigs is known to have various effects upon their behaviour. Social encounters in penned pigs normally take place at or near the feeding trough. These social encounters lead to clear-cut results when the hierarchial system has previously been well established. When growing pigs are allocated only about three-quarters of a square metre of pen each, there is a rise in severity of social encounters. When the stocking density is any heavier than this it is found that individual pigs, which are low in the social hierarchy, are unable to avoid the consequences of aggressive encounters. In consequence these pigs suffer more injury and reduced feeding opportunities. The productivity of the unit is thus adversely affected.

The consequences of agonistic behaviour between pigs are most severe among the adults. If a strange sow is introduced to an established group of sows, the collective aggressive behaviour of the group directed at the stranger is likely to be so severe that physical injury may be caused which can even result in the death of some animals. When two strange boars are first put together, they circle around and smell each other and in some cases may paw the ground. Deep-throated barking grunts may be made and jaw snapping engaged in, at this point. When fighting starts, the opponents adopt a shoulder to shoulder position applying side pressure against each other. Boars when fighting each other, tend to use the side of the mouth permitting the tusks to be brought into play as weapons. In this fashion, fighting boars attack the sides of their opponents bodies. Fighting may continued in this form for up to 1 hour before the submission of one animal or the other. The loser then disengages from the conflict and turns and runs away squealing loudly. With the other's dominance established the encounter ends. Mixing adult pigs together, therefore, is an operation which must be carried out with care. Tranquilizers and aerosol masking odours are used in commercial pig breeding and other pig establishments to minimize agonistic behaviour among pigs when mixing them.

# SUPPLEMENTARY READING

BALDWIN, B. A. (1969) The study of behaviour in pigs. *Br. Vet. J.*, *125*, 281–287.

DUTT, R. H., SIMPSON, B. C., CHRISTIAN, J. C. & BARNHART, C. E. (1959) Identification of preputial glands as the site of production of sexual odor in the boar. *J. Anim. Sci.*, *18*, 1557 (Abstract).

HAFEZ, E. S. E. & SIGNORET, J. P. (1969) Behaviour of swine. In: *The Behaviour of Domestic Animals*, ed. E. S. E. Hafez, 2nd ed., chapter 11. London: Baillière, Tindall & Cassell.

WYETH, G. S. F. & McBRIDE, G. (1964) Social behaviour of domestic animals. V. A note on sucking behaviour in young pigs. *Anim. Prod.*, *6*, 245–247.

# 8.

# Environmental Influences on Behaviour

## THE INFLUENCE OF CLIMATE

The adaptive mechanisms of cattle, living under various climatic conditions, have come under increasingly detailed study by animal scientists over the last two decades, but it is only recently that the behavioural aspects have been closely examined. Previously, most investigations were carried out under laboratory conditions and in circumstances of deliberate temperature control and fluctuation, but many researchers have since become aware of the immediate rewards of studying the animals ethologically. The differences in response to heat, solar radiation and the immediate environment are thus becoming better known, and they are found to vary greatly between breeds and from one area to another.

The level of temperature at which the so-called European breeds of cattle are able to maintain a normal body temperature (the thermoneutral zone) is said to be about 0° to 20°C. Tropical breeds, on the other hand, are able to maintain a normal body temperature in ambient temperatures of about 22° to 37°C. There is evidence to suggest that some tropical breeds are even able to carry on normal activity and locomotion, in temperatures in excess of 37°C. Both types are, however, found to use behavioural methods in attempting to control their temperatures.

### Thermoregulation

Possibly the first and most easily recognizable evidence of adaptive behaviour in cattle are the movements directed towards seeking shade, particularly when ambient heat greatly exceeds body heat. The fact, that European cattle show a stronger motivation towards shade-seeking and have a greater shade-dependence than tropical or subtropical breeds, is not unexpected. Thus, though the behaviour of both Aberdeen Angus and Brahman cattle in cloudy, overcast conditions is much the same, when the two breeds are in conditions of direct solar radiation with little or no air movement, differences become apparent. There is a definite change in the behaviour of Aberdeen Angus, which seek out shade and consequently spend less time grazing than do Brahman cattle, which are less inclined to undertake adaptive behaviour under such conditions. On the other hand, the adaptive behaviour of the Aberdeen Angus is much less marked if there is good air movement, regardless of the change in temperature.

Differences in behaviour, however, are not so simple. Tropical mammals, too, need shade and relief from high degrees of heat. The extent of shade-seeking and of shade-dependence varies within the tropical breeds themselves. Cattle living in tropical rain forest and equatorial areas of the world show a greater need for shade than those living in sparse or semi-arid areas where rainfall is low and shade limited. It has been found that the Dwarf Shorthorn breed of cattle in Nigeria may spend as long as 4·5 hours resting in the shade during the day and, to compensate, as long as 3·5 hours grazing during the night. In this way their behaviour may be nearer that of the temperate breeds, such as Aberdeen Angus, Hereford and Holstein, than that of the Brahman breed.

Experiments have been carried out on the behaviour of a herd of Friesians split up into groups. Each group sought shade in a different manner under slightly different conditions of heat.

## Ingestion

An early behavioural change during high temperatures is a reduction in food intake. This may arise not only from the shade-seeking activities of the animal, but also from a reduced desire for food. Consequential results are an alteration in eliminative behaviour and a general decline in performance. Cattle feeding in semi-arid areas, however, often do not lose weight under these conditions; indeed they may gain weight. In Israel cattle eating less than half the amount ingested by cattle in Britain are often fed twice as much concentrate in their food. It is suggested that in this way cattle in semi-arid areas manage to survive satisfactorily. It has been found that samples of crude tropical forage may contain 66% more crude protein and less crude fibre than pastures of clipped forage. The forage available in semi-arid areas, although sparsely distributed, also shows a greater variety of protein than in some temperate areas. It is desirable that cattle which are transferred to such regions should be permitted to graze selectively.

In subtropical conditions cattle often reduce their water-intake to once every 3 days. In areas with low rainfall and a long dry season, cattle normally graze up to 6 or 8 km from the nearest watering place, but a proximity to water of 19 km may be enough to maintain a satisfactory degree of health and survival. Often the entire grazing area around the water is completely eaten out. In such cases it is the cattle which are strongest and the most resourceful foragers, which can expect to continue as viable livestock. As the dry season approaches, there is a noticeable reduction in water-intake, and if breeds of tropical cattle are deprived of water, the nature of their metabolism enables them to put on fat. They are able to survive in this manner for up to 2 months, until the fat reserve is reabsorbed. By virtue of their long intestines (much longer than those of European breeds), cattle of tropical origin are able to reduce the volume of urine and faeces, thereby conserving much of the liquid contained therein. It is this character which enables these animals to travel on foot for hundreds of kilometres to grazing areas, with the aid of experienced drovers, and to arrive there alive.

## Breeding Behaviour

The sexual and reproductive behaviours of farm animals can be influenced by climatic factors (Figs 13 and 14).

In the tropics sexual behaviour is affected by seasonal conditions. Young animals have a much reduced chance of survival if parturition has taken place during seasonal weather of an extreme nature. Consequently natural reproductive activities occur more often during certain periods of the year than during others. Generally, the sex drive of the male if found to be least apparent during the hours of greatest solar radiation; in the case of sheep, temporary impotence often occurs. In certain areas as in Africa where there is only one rainy season per year, breeding is largely restricted to that period.

Observations on the reproductive behaviour of male goats in the West Indies have shown that these animals are able to mate

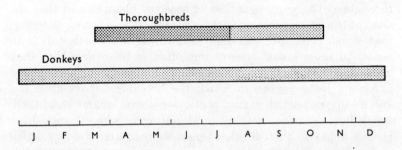

Fig. 13.   The span of the breeding season in donkeys and thoroughbred horses in a tropical latitude (18°N) in terms of the spread of oestrus. The presence of a seasonal feature of breeding in horses and the existence of a more intensive breeding phase at the start of annual breeding activity are shown.

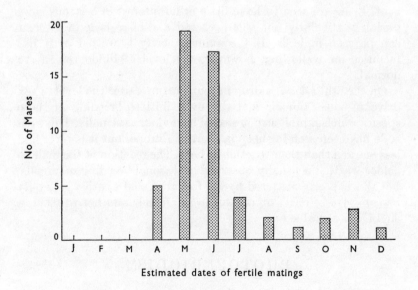

Fig. 14.   A histogram of fertile matings in a herd of free ranging Exmoor ponies. The full span of the breeding season is only revealed by the less fertile mares.

throughout the year regardless of seasonal changes and that the level of the libido remains fairly constant. It was found, however, that sexual behaviour was depressed during wet weather. It is an aspect of these goats' general reproductive behaviour that they are least active during rainy periods.

Among those species in which the breeding behaviour is not specifically restricted to any particular season of the year, there are definite occasions within the 24-hour cycle when the sex drive is more apparent than at other times. Many breeds of sheep, which maintain an all year round sex drive, are known to mate more often around sunset and sunrise; particularly the latter. As the onset of oestrus in ewes usually takes place at night, the period around dawn has the highest incidence of mating. It has been verified in Brazil, among Merino, Romney Marsh and Corriedale breeds of sheep, that oestrus occurred at night in 75% of cases, and a similar pattern has been observed in Cheviots in Britain.

In general the level of libido in the male is reduced and even, on occasions, negated or negative under conditions of intense heat. Boars are seen to have little or no interest in oestrous sows during particularly hot weather, and a similar lack of interest can be seen in bulls. If the animal's body is wetted or it has facilities for wallowing, however, the level of libido returns to normal.

On the other hand, a drop in temperature raises the level of sex drive in some animals and can even initiate breeding in those species which exhibit strong sexual behaviour seasonally. This attitude has been seen in sheep in Central Europe, but it is rarer and less marked than their reaction to heat. The reaction of the male to colder weather is usually observed in seasonal breeding mammals, but this is partly obscured by the fact that cold weather generally has an adverse effect on oestrus in the female and hot weather, a slightly favourable one.

# PHOTOPERIODISM

Probably the main environmental factor influencing sexual behaviour in seasonal breeders, such as horses and sheep, is the ratio of light and dark during the 24-hour cycles throughout these seasons.

The photoperiodic influence, however, is a complex one combining the intensity or quality of light with the relative duration of light and darkness. The positive influence of photoperiodism on the animal's sexual behaviour is usually associated with an increasing light to darkness ratio. Some species, however, show a corresponding escalation in sexual behaviour when this ratio is reversed.

Experimentation and observation have shown that the manipulation of the photoperiodic influence on reproductive behaviour is often possible by artificially advancing the season. An earlier onset of oestrus of this kind usually levels out as the season progresses. One aspect of the manipulation of the daylength is that it can advance the development of puberty in the young female or, alternatively, can slow it down.

Illuminatory experiments, attempting to influence or to specify the ungulates' sense of photoperiodism, have shown the important part that the hours of darkness and light play in engendering oestrus in female sheep and goats and, to a lesser extent, in mares. A reduction in the hours of light has successfully induced photoperiodic and behavioural responses bringing about oestrus. On the other hand, a progressive daily increase in the hours of darkness has successfully brought oestrus to an end. It has been found that a progressive decrease in the amount of daylight is not the only successful way of encouraging oestrus; a simple fixed ratio of light and darkness has also proved successful. There is also evidence that not only light, but an unbroken duration of darkness influences oestrus, and that patterns in the duration of darkness can bring forward the beginning of the breeding season in sheep. Less is known about the effects of illumination on oestrus in the equidae, but experiments with Shetland ponies, which have a very short and well-defined breeding season and with ponies in south-east Asia, have shown that mares can be made to come into oestrus by exposure to prolonged periods of light out of season.

There has been less research done on male sexual behaviour and the degree to which it is subject to seasonal variations. It is often assumed that the male will always be ready to serve at the time the female comes into oestrus. Observations were made in Canada on the breeding rhythms of male Saanen and Toggenberg goats in natural light conditions (Fig. 15). It was found during the period of prolonged daylight lasting from around April until September, sexual activity and potency were relatively weaker, but that the

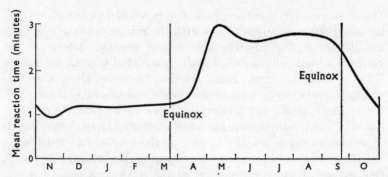

Fig. 15. The season trends in sex drive in nine goats as shown in their mean reaction times. Two principal phases are recognizable as plateaux in winter and summer. Note the two short periods of high and low sex drive after autumnal and vernal equinoxes respectively.

reaction times returned to normal in October. Thus it was deduced that there is not so much a total inhibition of the sex drive in summer, but rather a great reduction, whereby the drive is more easily satisfied and for longer reaction times.

## BEHAVIOUR IN TRANSIT

Observations have shown that cattle become calm and co-operative with handlers and with each other, when travelling long distances by rail. When travelling together in an enclosed area, they rarely move about to alter their position or seek another part of the wagon and do so only when the train has stopped, or is stopping or starting. They travel facing the side of the wagon and with their bodies at right angles to the direction of travel. This appears to be the most convenient position when seeking optimum comfort and space for balance, and for minimizing injury, should they lose their balance. It has been found that cattle with longish horns usually adopt a position where their heads are resting upon the backs of the adjacent animals; this makes for easier breathing as well as avoiding injury.

On long journeys it is often over 24 hours before some of the animals seek rest by lying down, but others avoid doing so for the entire journey. They usually lie down in groups of three or four

84

after one animal has made the initial move, and tend to do so at one end of the wagon. The remainder of the group will avoid trampling these animals as much as is possible, quickly moving any hoof which is brought down on the body of a recumbent animal. When given the opportunity to rest while disembarked at yards in sidings, they move to the water trough or walk about for a very short period, even when food is clearly visible, and feed only after their thirsts have been quenched.

At the beginning of the journey urination and defaecation in the wagon is frequent, but this declines as the animals adjust. Cattle which have had neither food nor drink during a long journey, sometimes expel small dry pellets of dung and may still urinate.

The hazards to which animals being transported by sea are vulnerable are numerous. When entering equatorial regions cattle are subject to heat stress. There is a constant danger of injury in rough weather; for instance horses need plenty of head room at sea. Cattle are highly susceptible to injury and illness during sea voyages and considerable medicinal and nutritional supplies are needed, if they are to reach their destination in good health.

In tropical areas cattle moving on the hoof are liable to infection, en route. Journeys of hundreds of kilometres are still undertaken to reach many distant destinations at the coast. It is estimated that 200 000 head per year are moved in this way from the breeding areas of the north of Nigeria and inland, to the cattle markets in the French-speaking countries and along the coast. After such a journey of 2 weeks or more, cattle often become infected with animal sleeping sickness. Sick animals have to be slaughtered en route to avoid slowing down the remainder of herd. The longer the journey takes the more likely the animals are to lose weight and, consequently, their value in the market.


# SOCIAL DENSITY

One aspect of the behaviour of animals in close proximity, is the strong allelomimetic tendencies which they display. This behaviour, whereby one individual is influenced by the grazing and drinking activities, eliminative behaviour or movement of others, is seen in a clearer light when the animal is placed in isolation, out of sight of any of its herd (or flock) mates and confined there. The animal shows visible signs of stress and its habit patterns become disrupted. Its intake of food and water declines and it makes constant efforts to rejoin the main group if it can possibly do so. Some sheep and horses have in fact been shown to decline all food and drink when totally isolated, even though both food and water may be immediately available. The isolation of an animal from its herd should therefore be avoided whenever possible, as the effects of this treatment on the animal can often be as undesirable as overcrowding.

Excessive social density in animals frequently results in restlessness, fighting and a disruption of daily routines of behaviour. All members of the group seem to be similarly affected, whether they are directly involved in the agonistic episodes or not.

# SUPPLEMENTARY READING

DE ALBA, J., VILLA CORTA, E. & ULLOA, G. (1961) Influence of natural service on length of oestrus in the cow. *Anim. Prod.*, *3*, 327–330.

DU MESNIL DU BUISSON, F. & SIGNORET, J. P. (1962) Influences de facteurs externes sur le déclenchement de la puberté chez la truie. *Annls. Zootech.*, *11*, 53–59.

DURAN DEL CAMPO, A. (1961) Artificial insemination in sheep. The efficiency of teaser rams in detecting ewes on heat. *Agronomia Vet. téc. pract. rur.*, *11*, 3–4. (*Anim. Breed Abstr.* (1962), *30*, No. 1107).

HEITMAN, H. & HUGHES, E. H. (1949) The effects of air temperature and relative humidity on the physiological well-being of swine. *J. anim. Sci.*, *8*, 171–181.

LEES, J. L. (1965) Some aspects of competition among farm animals. *J. agric. Soc. Univ. Coll. Wales, Aberyst.*, *46*, 15–22.

MOUNT, L. E. (1963) Environmental temperature preferred by the young pig. *Nature*, *199*, 1212–1213.

NERSESJAN, S. S. (1959) The use of vasectomised bulls as biological stimulators in controlling infertility in cows. *Trudy erevan. zoovet. Inst.*, no. 23. (*Anim. Breed Abstr.* (1962), *30*, No. 220).

PETROPAVLOVSKII, V. V. & RYKOVA, A. I. (1958) The stimulation of sexual functions in cows. *Trudy ul'yanov. sel'.-khoz. Inst.*, *5*, (2), 193–199. (*Anim. Breed. Abstr.* (1961), *29*, No. 798).

POLIKARPOVA, E. F. (1960) Biological characters in livestock reproduction. *Trudȳ Inst. Morf. Žhivot.*, no. 31, 26–34. (*Anim. Breed Abstr.* (1961), *29*, No. 1506).

SADLEIR, R. M. F. S. (1968) Reproductive responses to the environment in mammals. *J. psychosom. Res.*, *12*, 3–9.

SUTTON, G. D., FOURIE, P. D. & RETIEF, J. S. (1967) The behaviour of cattle in transit by rail. *Jl S. Afr. vet. med. Ass.*, *38*, (2), 153–156.

TEMBROK, G. (1963) Acoustic behaviour of mammals. In: *Acoustic Behaviour of Animals*, ed. R.-G. Busnel, pp. 751–783. Centre National de Recherches Zoo-techniques, France. Amsterdam: Elsevier.

# 9.
# Managemental Ethology

THE circumstances of domestication necessarily impose restraints on the behaviour of farm animals. Animals are customarily restrained by one of several methods. These include:

1. The application of physical force
2. The manoeuvring of animals by anticipation of their behaviour
3. Control by the application of mechanical disadvantage
4. The imposition of training to regulate behaviour
5. The control of behaviour by the use of drugs

## APPLICATION OF FORCE

The use of direct force in controlling the behaviour of animals is best exemplified by the variety of 'crushes' or stocks that are in use on many farm premises for the tight restriction of movement in the larger farm animals. Crushes of various types are in operation for controlling cattle, for example, but the best forms of crushes are those which allow an animal to be funnelled down a narrowing passage into the crush section. At the exit of the crush there should be a small collecting yard where animals which have already passed through the crush may be seen by the animal entering or within the crush. Crushing arrangements, which make use of this broad principle, allow large numbers of cattle to be examined individually and closely in a short space of time with the least amount of danger to themselves and to those handling them. Such crushing techniques allow mass treatment of herd, flock, etc., for such operations as vaccination, drenching, ear-tagging, blood sampling, tuberculin testing, pregnancy diagnosing, branding, spraying and dehorning. Many of these operations can cause animals to become so alarmed that they respond behaviourally in ways which frequently cause injury to themselves. Whilst restrained within stocks, cattle frequently attempt to escape by

88

pushing forwards. They also frequently attempt to push their hind limbs against one side or other of the stocks. The stocks, therefore, should be constructed with solid sides so that it is impossible for an animal to put its hind leg between spars since, when this happens, serious injury to the limb is likely. After stocks have been in use by a number of animals they tend to become slippery underfoot with the excreta of these animals, and it may be necessary to improve the footing within the stocks by the addition of ash or sand from time to time. When crushes possess some yolk arrangement which grips a restrained animal by the neck, it is important for there to be an efficient quick release mechanism which allows the animal's neck to be released quickly, should its limbs slip from under it and cause it to fall within the stock. This is particularly important when large animals such as bulls are being put into stocks. Their weight prevents them from being raised manually should they fall to the ground. Fixed crushes in which a string of animals can be restrained tightly behind one another, perhaps with intervening bars separating two or three of them, are known as races. This form of crush is very suitable for a close inspection of a large number of animals in a short time.

Stocks for horses are sometimes employed when an animal is to be examined standing per rectum, for example. Such stocks are also suitable means of restraint when some operation to the feet is being carried out on a fractious horse. Stock sizes vary with the type of horse to be examined. It is also essential that they should be extremely solid. A horse in close restraining stocks, which finds the stocks moving or hears the parts moving, is very likely to become overexcited and to lash out in a frenzy of kicking in a manner which is difficult to control.

## ANTICIPATION OF BEHAVIOUR

Anticipating an animal's movement is undoubtedly the best means of exercising some control over its behaviour. This is particularly true when the handling of loose animals is being attempted. The handling of such animals presents a very real problem to those who deal with livestock and many livestock owners view this task with some anxiety. Loose animals are best controlled when they are gathered into tight groups of their own kind. Pigs, sheep

Fig. 16.   Head leverage and straddling in the restraint of sheep. (drawing)

and cattle for example are much more easily handled by this means.

It is principally with regard to cattle that the problem of handling of loose animals is greatest. In many forms of cattle husbandry, calves are already well grown before they are required to be handled for the first time. Such calves are difficult to catch and eventually to control. A full-grown calf, unaccustomed to being handled, may show different forms of behaviour when approached. An initial state of alertness is usually observed. The animal directs its attention exclusively towards the source of the approaching danger and its behaviour reveals that it is conscious of the principal stimulant in its immediate environment. Its head is directed towards this source, and its eyes, ears and tail are moved in ways indicating its total concern with the person approaching. Closer approach towards the calf usually induces a state of alarm or fear. A group of animals will quickly share this state of alarm by signals generated within the group which are understood by all the others of the group. Close herding results; the animals pack more tightly together; they move more rapidly; their heads are held up; there is likely to be some bellowing. Animals in this state have been described as being fully adrenalized. In this condition they offer more resistance to handling. Further stimulation of these animals will result in the development of a stage of panic behaviour during which calculated behaviour is abandoned and a resort to flight takes place. This change sometimes occurs very gradually among calves, but on other occasions it can occur in an instant. Rapid changes in such a state of alarm are more common among calves which have had some prior experience of unpleasant association with humans.

To control the behaviour of calves in this state, the approach by the handler towards the calf should be quiet, even in pace, but cautious. During this type of approach the calf will commence to move away, either forwards or backwards. The handler should then modify his approach, either to the left or to the right, so as to cut off the intended route of escape. After one or two intention movements by the calf the animal will then direct its flight towards a corner. The expert handler makes use of this knowledge of animal behaviour to time his attempt at catching the animal to coincide with the time when the animal's head is directed towards a corner. When the calf is being caught it is important to grip its lower jaw and to raise it and pull it sharply to one side. Gripping the lower jaw is more effective in controlling cattle than catching

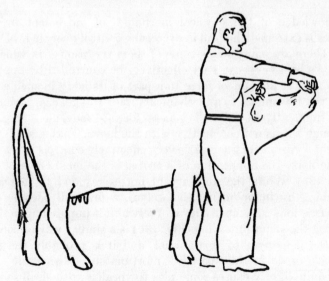

Fig. 17.   Head leverage method of restraining cattle. (tracing)

the nose. Small calves in particular resent their noses being held. This part of the body is apparently very sensitive and also the restriction to breathing induces further panic in the subject.

In directing the movements of animals individually or in groups, the expert handler makes use of the fact that animals apparently regard as part of the person approaching anything which is held in the hand and extended outwards on either side. This way one person can extend his presence considerably to either side and thereby cut off a very large escape area for an animal which is loose.

This general rule is not applicable to pigs. They do not appear to be susceptible to this form of control. Pigs are best blocked from their escape route by placing some solid object, such as a board, at ground level directly in the line of their escape. Once a pig has selected a line of escape it is not so likely to deviate from this line as other animals are and, when this route is blocked in the manner described, the pig is frequently stopped altogether in its flight.

# APPLICATION OF MECHANICAL DISADVANTAGE

A knowledge of the physical mechanics of movement in each species is extremely helpful in exercising control over their behaviour. There are many ways, some of them traditional, in which an animal's behaviour can very effectively be controlled by applying some modest amount of force to a part of its body in such a way as to put the animal to a mechanical disadvantage, e.g. raising the head frequently restrains the general forward movement (Fig. 17), although this is not so effective with the horse. Taking some form of tight control over the muzzle very effectively controls behaviour. In the horse the application of a twitch is the most effective way (Fig. 18B). While the majority of horses respond to increasing twitching by immobilizing themselves, a few will become even more fractious when such a form of restraint is imposed upon them. Snaring the snout of the pig (Fig. 18D) is a similar way of controlling the behaviour of this animal, and it is probably the most effective of all in this species. Unfortunately, snaring the snout even quite lightly causes some pigs to vocalize with shrill screaming sounds which pig handlers may not be able to tolerate for long.

Fig. 18.   (A) Prevention of self-grooming in a horse with a neck cradle.
(B) Restraint of behaviour in a horse using a twitch on the upper
lip. (C) Simple method of blindfolding a horse to lead it where it
is reluctant to go. (D) Control of a mature pig with a snout snare.
(drawings)

Examples of the ways in which the most anterior part of the
animal can be secured to effect overall control are shown in Figs
16, 17 and 18.

The limb movements of an animal have to be controlled in many
circumstances when kicking or stamping would endanger other
animals in close proximity or persons handling the animal. Kicking
with the hind limbs can be controlled in a variety of ways (Figs 19
and 20). Restraint in the region of the hocks which, to a large

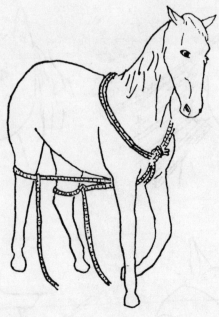

Fig. 19.   Restraint of a mare with 'service hobbles' prior to hand mating. (drawing)

Fig. 20.   The application of an udder-kinch to control forward hind limb movement in a cow. (drawing)

extent, immobilizes the Achilles tendon can be used as a method of controlling kicking. Similarly raising one foreleg above the knee with a rope will rapidly restrain stamping. Full-grown cattle can have their hind limbs fairly effectively immobilized by the application of restricting ropes which apply pressure around the abdomen of the animal while drawing the head backwards with a rope round the horns. Raising the tail-head vertically in cattle (Fig. 21) can also effectively immobilize the hind limb for short periods.

Fig. 21.   Restraint of hind limb movement in a stalled cow by uprooting the tail. (drawing)

Animals which are being given medical treatment of various kinds may have to be lifted from the ground to reduce opposition. This, of course, is applicable only in the case of small livestock. The way in which a foal can be restrained and held for lifting is shown in Fig. 22.

The purpose of all of these forms of restraint is to immobilize the animal for a short period of time, so that some procedure considered necessary for its welfare can be carried out with minimum discomfort to the patient and maximum safety to the operator. These procedures should not be based on the infliction of

Fig. 22.   The advised method of restraining the behaviour of young foals.
(drawing)

pain upon the animal. It is emphasized, therefore, that such procedures are intended not to cause harm to the animal but tempor-
arily to place it in a state of mechanical disadvantage.

# TRAINING

Farm animal behaviour can be controlled quite readily following
fairly simple training procedures. Animals quickly learn the routines of feeding, for example, and it is usually possible to lure animals into required situations by methods which they come to
recognize by repetition. Animals also learn to associate certain
sounds with certain husbandry routines; a great repertoire of
conditioned reflexes quickly become established in most farm animals in this way and by the use of the human voice. Skilful exploi-
tation of conditioning, which is known to have occurred, can allow
the experienced stock handler to exercise a good deal of control
over the behaviour of his animals. The use of calls, sounds of
buckets, whistles, etc., can provide quick labour-saving methods
of assembling animals. All farm animals show a tendency to herd
and one can easily impose upon an untrained animal, the training

which has been acquired by others. This is done by including it for a short time within the group, and then permitting it to share in the experiences of the group as a whole.

# USE OF DRUGS

The use of drugs in the control of an animal is sometimes necessary to avoid excessive muscular resistance. In the past, limited knowledge of the action and use of drugs sometimes prevented the satisfactory control of behaviour. Today, however, the range of modern chemical agents of varied pharmacological activities makes it possible to alter an animal's behaviour by tranquilization and immobilization. Today tranquilizers are commonly used when individual animals have to be subjected, for a period, to forms of total restraint or handling to which they are unaccustomed, and which would likely induce in them a state of panic which would be detrimental to their health were it attempted by other means. Tranquilization during transportation, for example, has much to commend it in circumstances when individual animals are being dealt with. Total immobilization is a very radical form of restraint and is one which is extremely useful and warranted in many emergencies for the welfare of the subject. The use of an immobilizing agent is restricted by law to a veterinary surgeon.

From what has been said in this chapter it will be noted that there are a great variety of ways in which behaviour of livestock can be controlled. Many of them, time-proven, are well-known to experienced stockmen. Knowledge of others is acquired by the veterinary surgeon during his training in pharmacology and are necessary chemotherapeutic aids, the use of which is confined to the qualified practitioner.

# SUPPLEMENTARY READING

MILLER, W. C. & ROBERTSON, E. D. S. (1943) *Practical Animal Husbandry*. Edinburgh and London: Oliver & Boyd.

# Part III
# REPRODUCTION

# 10.
# Sexual Behaviour

## THE MALE

### Male Sex Drive

Sex drive in the entire male amongst farm animals is commonly referred to as libido. This drive develops at puberty and, after maturation, persists at a fairly constant level for the remainder of the animal's lifespan. Libido or male sex drive is dependent, basically, on the production of testosterone by the testis, but in an individual animal the typical level of the sex drive is predetermined by inherited characteristics.

Some variations in the level of male sex drive are to be observed and these can have quite considerable consequences in farm economics. In the bull, libido varies in degree between age groups and between breed types. In general, a lower level of libido is found in beef than in dairy breeds. Comparing the species, the highest levels of libido are generally noted among the seasonal breeding animals, for example rams. Clearly those species which concentrate their breeding season into relatively short periods require high levels of libido for effective reproduction during that time. The level of sex drive may change as a consequence of various factors: there are the physical changes that occur in ageing bulls which are known to reduce their sex drive. Quite clearly, an animal which is experiencing discomfort or even pain during movement in mounting will, in time, have his breeding behaviour impaired. It is also strongly suspected that adverse experiential factors can cause sexual inhibitions in all stud animals.

While low libido in free-living animals is species self-limiting, in domestication unwise selection can permit its propagation; and there is evidence that this has occurred in some of the beef breeds of cattle. It is recognized by practical flockmasters that, in some breeds of sheep, the rams have higher levels of sex drive than in others. There is also growing suspicion that certain breeds of pigs produce boars with inferior libido. Impaired or inferior libido is not always inherited. Obesity in stud animals often contributes to low libido. Some skeletal defects such as arthritis are also a common cause of poor breeding behaviour. Clinical studies in recent years have confirmed that many impotent boars, for example, suffer arthritis of the hip joint.

An interesting phenomenon of male sex drive is one which is associated with its total absence. When entire male animals experience complete loss of their sex drive for some reason or other, they seek out the company of other male animals of the same species. The bachelor groupings (Figs 23 and 24) which result when such male animals gather together is a phenomenon which has been observed in many species of free-living animals. Bachelor groupings can be noted when large numbers of bulls run together. They are also seen among rams during the long non-breeding season of the year. The purpose of bachelor groupings is to suppress further any libido that individual males might have, and such close male groupings quite clearly show successful adaptation amongst their members.

Among the seasonal breeding species it is noted that, during each breeding season, the level of libido reached or attained by an individual remains fairly characteristic for it until ageing effects occur. Here again we see the genetic basis of libido at work. This genetic basis is of great significance as a variety of experiments have testified. One researcher has reported on the uniformly poor level of libido characteristic of each individual in a set of monozy-

Fig. 23.    Bachelor-grouping among Blackface rams in summer. (tracing)

Fig. 24.   Bachelor-grouping of Highland bulls. (tracing)

gous triplet bulls. Extensive Swedish studies have put the genetic basis of libido in bulls beyond doubt by showing the similarity of sex drive among pairs of identical twins even when these pairs were separated and subjected to quite different forms of husbandry. The selection of stud animals likely to have good libido is clearly called for in order to preserve breed fertility. In this connection it it is important to stress that there is no significant connection between good sexual behaviour in the stud animal and the production of good quality semen. Highly fertile semen may be obtained from stud animals with poor libido and conversely, bulls, rams and other male animals may show excellent libido but poor sperm production. Though these two characters are unrelated, the selection of stud animals with their potential sexual behaviour in mind is of importance as, without good libido, even good quality sperm does not ensure successful breeding.

The level of libido in a particular male has been assessed by experimental workers and this factor can undoubtedly be gauged fairly accurately. Note can be taken of an animal's performance under sexually exhausting conditions: the number of mating failures over a period of time or, more simply, the reaction time. By ensuring that a fairly constant stimulus is afforded, measurement of the male's reaction time, namely the time taken for the animal to mount a female, is as simple and reliable a method as any of estimating his libido.

The libido of billy goats was tested in this way at weekly intervals over a period of a year and a close correlation was found to exist between the estimated libido and the year's successful matings.

Protracted reaction times have been noted in bulls of a certain type of temperament. Although the temperament of an animal can only be assessed fairly subjectively, those who have close contact with the animal and are able to make repeated observations on its behaviour can make quite sound assessments of temperament. While the majority of bulls have temperaments which could be described as stable, a certain proportion are well known to be aggressive. Yet others are found to have temperaments or dispositions which could only be described as apprehensive. Such bulls are usually found to have very protracted reaction times. It is reasonable to suppose that these animals have acquired inhibitions, which prevent their effective mating behaviour, through a reduction in libido. The problem of reduced libido in the male is of no small importance. Studies have shown that it is probably the most common problem encountered in stud animals and the one which most frequently leads to their being culled in due course. Indeed, it is likely to be the most common cause of infertility in the male farm animal. Clearly when reaction times extend into periods of about an hour, an animal of this type must be condemned as unsound.

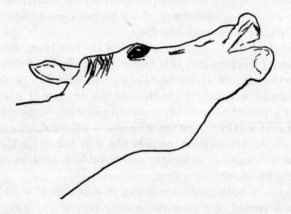

Fig. 25.    Flehmen in a stallion. Note constriction of nostrils and lip-curl.
(tracing)

Fig. 26.  Vigorous nudging in the form of butting in breeding goats. (tracing)

## *Male Sexual Patterns*

When a male animal is consorting with a breeding female in oestrus various forms of male sexual behaviour are to be observed. One of the most common characteristics of male sexual behaviour is the olfactory reflex of flehmen (Fig. 25). Among the farm animals the boar is the only one which fails to show this reflex. In flehmen the animal raises and extends the head and neck, and retracts and stretches the upper lip. Other precoital components of behaviour seen, tend to be species specific. Sheep and goats, however, have many items of courtship behaviour in common. These include: nosing of the female's perineum, nudging the female, flehmen, flicking out of the tongue, striking out with a forelimb and low-pitched bleating sounds. In addition to these behavioural features, the male goat also spills small quantities of urine particularly on to his forelegs. Butting of the female's hindquarters is also occasionally seen in both of these species (Fig. 26). It can also be noted in bulls. False mounting attempts are sometimes shown by rams and billy goats; this behavioural feature is also seen in horses. Bulls often pump their tailheads up and down during precoitus and during the same period may pass small quantities of faeces which become spread around their hindquarters by their tail action. Stallions bite the flanks and sides of mares. Boars 'root' into the flanks of sows with their snouts.

There are, however, certain major behavioural activities common to all male farm animals. These are:

1. Threat Displays
2. Challenges
3. Territorial Activities
4. Female Seeking and Driving
5. Female Tending

Although these behavioural activities tend to flow into each other they are easier to study individually.

*Threat Displays.* These are usually produced by animals in a stationary position. The threat display of the bull is in fact a physiological state of fight or flight. In this state the animal hunches his shoulders, flexes his neck and shows protrusion of the eyeballs and erection of hair along the dorsum. During a threat display the bull turns shoulder-on towards the threatened object. The threat display of the stallion involves rearing on his hind legs. The boar in threat display turns his side towards the threatened object, holds his head down and emits barking sounds. Threat displays are rarely shown by rams towards humans but, nevertheless, forms of threat are exhibited in the presence of other potential aggressors and in these circumstances the threat display usually involves vigorous stamping of a forefoot.

*Challenges.* Challenging behaviour among male animals is typically seen when there is an opportunity for several males to form pairs. When challenges are taken up the outcome of the challenge eventually determines the peck order or hierarchy. Status in the peck order also affords sexual status in free-breeding groups of animals. Under these circumstances the male at the top of the peck order may perform all the breeding with the available females, to the exclusion of males lower down the peck order. Under domestication this type of circumstance is not usually permitted to develop. Nevertheless, stockbreeders are not unfamiliar with 'boss bulls' and 'boss rams'.

The most dramatic example of challenging among the farm animals is shown by the bull. The bull's challenge display has

Fig. 27.   Three components of the full behavioural pattern of male display
in the bull. (drawing)

three principal components (Fig. 27) which run closely together
but may occur in various arrangements. The three components are:
  *Bellowing.* The bull stands stationary and bellows repeatedly
  with his head extended. Bellowing takes the form of long chains
  of vocalizations which have repeated breaks in pitch.
  *Pawing.* The bull paws vigorously at the ground with a forefoot
  with his head lowered. This pawing which may break up the soil

107

has a follow-through foot action which effectively scoops soil upwards throwing it over the animal's back.

*Horning.* The bull rubs the side of his face and his horns vigorously against the surface of the ground. Indoors this may be practised against a wall or a post. Out of doors horning is often practised in a kneeling position and is displayed with some vigour.

*Territorial Activities.* Territorial behaviour is demonstrated far less by the farm animals than by many of the free-living wildlife species. The latter may de-bark trees extensively and disperse various secretions around the perimeter of their territories. Nevertheless the domesticated male animal does engage in behaviour which can be described as being territorial. Pawing and horning behaviour by bulls effectively bares patches of earth out of doors and these earth patches located throughout his territory are clearly a claim to possession of a given area. Stallions also claim territory; they do this at pasture where they urinate and defaecate at selected spots. Given suitable territory they mark it in this fashion, returning from time to time to defaecate again in the same places. Some horses also bite bark off trees although there is some doubt as to whether this is true territorial behaviour.

*Female Seeking and Driving.* The seeking out activity of male animals for females in oestrus goes on continuously under free-breeding conditions in the open. The experienced male animal is capable of detecting the pro-oestrus phase in the female. After locating a female in this breeding state the male will consort with her and from time to time will engage in driving behaviour. The male may drive the female forward in differing ways. Stallions force mares to move forward by nipping their hindquarters and often biting them in the region of the hocks. Bulls may butt cows' hindquarters. Sheep and goats push females from behind using their shoulders. Boars nose into sows vigorously forcing them to move forwards.

*Female Tending.* Tending behaviour is displayed by the farm animals when opportunities permit. Typically the male maintains close association, sometimes close bodily contact, with the female whilst grazing with her. While consorting with her, he also periodically engages in nudging behaviour (Fig. 28). This prompts the female to move forwards. The female in oestrus responds to this stimulation by adopting a stationary stance, so facilitating mating. Standing firm is then seen as the positive response to nudging and provides reciprocal stimulation for the male animal. Nudging, in some form or other, can be seen in the precoital behaviour of all the farm animals and is prominent in the courtship behaviour of rams. Rams nudge by pushing with their shoulders and also striking the hindlimbs of the ewes with their forefeet. Butting is another form of nudging shown by all the ruminants (bulls, rams and billy goats). Once mating has occurred the breeding partners often

Fig. 28.  Nudging behaviour between boar and gilt. (drawing)

exhibit a so-called tending-bond over a period of time. Both sexes contribute to this temporary alliance. In the tending-bonds of most of the farm animals there are moments when the male animal rests his chin over the hindquarters of the female from time to time. This chinning behaviour is best seen in cattle (Fig. 29) but it also occurs in the other species.

## The Stimulation of Male Sexual Behaviour

Various stimuli are known to affect male sex drive. Some bulls are most stimulated when permitted to breed out of doors. Some male animals prefer females of certain colours or other characteristics, and it is apparent that some females have greater stimulus value

Fig. 29. Dorsal views of a cow showing areas where a bull with a chin raddle has made contact before (A) and during (B) oestrus. The markings provide evidence of courtship activities during both phases. (drawing)

than others. The basic stimulus for male sexual behaviour is less specific than those mentioned since the majority of male farm animals will mount and attempt to mate with dummy teasers; these may consist of no more than a trunk and four supports.

## THE FEMALE

### *Oestrus*

The normal mating state of the female animal is termed oestrus. Although the term 'in oestrus' applies principally to behaviour it must be acknowledged that it also describes some internal physiological processes. Although the two features of oestrus (behavioural and physiological) can occur separately this is rare and it is normal for them to exist simultaneously. When oestrus is shown in the female, behaviour in general changes and many of the animal's usual routines become disturbed. There is often an alteration and reduction in feeding and resting patterns, for example, but this is secondary to the essential characteristic of oestrous behaviour which is acceptance of the male, i.e. mating. Variations in the intensity of oestrous behaviour occur and we can recognize that this drive also varies from animal to animal. The level of oestrous drive in cattle is seen to range from intense to very mild. Oestrus can sometimes also be so subdued in cattle and in pigs as to be virtually undetectable; this condition has been referred to in the past as silent heat.

The principal behavioural signs of oestrus in *cattle* are as follows. There may be an increase in what could generally be termed as excitement. The oestrous cow bellows increasingly. Grooming activities, in the form of licking other animals, are also increased. Typically the oestrous cow indulges in a great deal of mounting of other cattle. When several cattle in a group have been prompted to mount each other, through the initial activity of the oestrous cow, it may become difficult for an observer to identify the oestrous cow in the group. However, when one animal in particular is standing to be mounted by others it is possible to identify it as the animal in oestrus. Oestrus lasts for a period of 12 to 24 hours and it is commonly observed to be of shortest duration in younger cattle.

Oestrous behaviour in *horses* also features a range of salient characteristics peculiar to this species. The intensity of the oestrous drive varies probably more than in any of the other farm species. A mare in heat (or in oestrus) typically adopts a urinating stance. During these periods of straddling, mucoid urine is ejected in small quantities which splash at the animal's heels. Following this, the animal maintains the straddling stance with the hindlimbs abducted and stretched backwards. The tail is elevated so as to be arched away from the perineum and the heels of one or other hind hoof are commonly seen to be tilted up off the ground so that only the toe of that hoof remains touching the ground. While this stance is maintained the animal shows flashing of the clitoris by repeated rhythmic contractions of the vulva. This oestrous display is perhaps the most elaborate one seen among the farm animals. The duration of oestrus is some 4 to 6 days on average but varies a great deal, some oestruses lasting only 1 day and others lasting up to 20 days. The duration of oestrus shortens as the breeding season progresses. It is also thought that oestrus periods among smaller breeds of horses are typically shorter than among large ones. Oestrous periods follow each other every 20 to 22 days.

The principal feature of oestrous behaviour in *pigs* is the adoption of a stationary posture in response to pressure applied on the back. In pig breeding practice this is sometimes done by an attendant sitting astride the animal. In response to this pressure the sow in true oestrus usually remains stationary, and short-eared breeds of pigs such as the Large White simultaneously show a stiff upward pricking of the ears which are also directed backwards. The onset and the termination of the oestrous period in the sow are gradual but the central period, which lasts about 24 hours on average, is quite well defined and is the period of high intensity sex drive. It is in this high intensity period that the standing reflex is most clearly shown. Oestrous sows are sometimes more restless than others, particularly when enclosed, and it is found that this restless behaviour is most marked during the hours of night. Mutual riding is occasionally seen in groups of pigs, one of which is in oestrus, but this is much less commonly observed than in cattle. Occasionally among groups of sows, one in particular is found to perform most of the riding behaviour when any other sow in the group is in oestrus.

Of all the farm animals, the *sheep* shows least behavioural evidence of oestrus. Heat in this animal is extremely difficult to detect if there is no ram with the ewe. When a ram is present the ewe coming into oestrus will usually seek out his company and consort with him for a period of several hours before oestrus proper commences. Many observers have noted that ewes in oestrus frequently initiate the first sexual contact with rams and thereafter follow the rams about in their grazing movements as long as heat persists. Oestrus can last for up to 3 days in some ewes although the normal period is recognized as being just over 24 hours. Mutual riding among ewes, one of which is in oestrus, has not been reported.

In some contrast to the sheep the signs of oestrus in *goats* are very marked indeed. The female in oestrus shows rapid tail waving actions during which the upright tail quivers very rapidly from side to side. This tail action resembles 'flagging' and is shown in frequent bursts which are repeated throughout oestrus. Oestrus lasts on average just over 24 hours. During this period the doe eats less than usual, has a tendency to roam and bleats very frequently.

*Onset of Oestrus.* Extensive observations confirm that the onset of oestrus in cattle occurs at random. Apparently onset can be at any hour of the day or night. There is a suggestion, however, that among cattle indigenous to tropical climates there is a much higher frequency of oestrus during the night. Similar observations have been reported in sheep in warm climates where it has been noted that approximately 75% of them commence oestrus during the night. Even in northern latitudes the commencement of oestrus in sheep is during the night in the majority of cases.

*Anoestrus.* Anoestrus is the condition in which female animals fail to show cyclic recurrence of oestrus. Anoestrus normally occurs when the animal is pregnant or when it is in its non-breeding season. Some animals such as sheep will occasionally show oestrus in the non-breeding season as will some pregnant animals. It has been estimated that 3% of pregnant animals also show oestrus. Oestrus during pregnancy has not infrequently been noted in mares, cattle and sheep. It has also been observed in sows. It is probably shown more often in the early stages of pregnancy but it has also been recorded in cattle during the last month of their 9 month gestational period. Further matings taking place during these oestrous periods do not result in fertilization.

## Post-parturient Oestrus

Some animals show oestrus very soon after parturition while others have a considerable time lag between parturition and the first subsequent oestrus. It seems that in species such as the ruminants, where fertilization involves a minimal amount of semen from the male animal, the uterus becomes completely contracted and involuted following parturition. On the other hand animals, such as horses and pigs, in which the fertilization process involves large volumes of semen, do not seem to have the same degree of post-parturient uterine involution and constriction.

*Horses.* The mare is the best example of a farm animal showing early oestrus postpartum. This early oestrus, called the foal heat, occurs on average 7 to 9 days after the birth of the foal and is often short and of lower fertility than subsequent heats. There is strong evidence to suggest however that under conditions of domestication the full potential fertility of foal heat is not always achieved. Under natural conditions, when a stallion is running continuously with the herd of mares, the foal heat can be as fully fertile as any subsequent heat. Under these conditions fertile oestruses seem to occur very early in the breeding season when the majority of mares are likely to be showing the foal heat.

*Pigs*. Doubt has been expressed about first accounts of oestrus in the sow postpartum. Although laboratory workers have failed to find any evidence of ovarian activity in sows which have recently farrowed, pigbreeders have reported on many occasions that sows show evidence of a 'false' heat about 3 days after farrowing. Scientific workers have also reported that some sows can be bred at this time but that these breedings are usually infertile. Under normal conditions of husbandry, the first oestrus noted in the sow is the one which follows weaning. Weaning normally takes place between 1 and 2 weeks following farrowing, commonly when the litter is about 6 weeks old. Some 3 to 5 days after weaning the majority of sows in good health will show oestrous behaviour.

*Cattle*. Cattle show a greater delay before the first oestrus after parturition. Under normal circumstances it is unusual for any oestrus to be shown within 35 days of calving. Indeed, if cattle are suckling their calves, oestrus may be delayed for several months.

*Sheep*. In those breeds of sheep which have fairly long breeding seasons some individuals do show oestrus about 5 to 7 weeks after lambing. If ewes are still suckling their lambs at this time, however, these oestruses are subdued and are not usually fertile. Under usual circumstances the first normal oestrus seen in sheep and in goats occurs in the breeding season following parturition.

# BIOSTIMULATION

It is now recognized that for oestrous responses to be shown in complete form in many farm animals it is necessary for some form of male stimulation to be provided. Male attendance which supplies prompting, as for example in the form of nudging, is now appreciated to be an important contributor to oestrous displays in females. This male influence on oestrous behaviour is termed biostimulation. Although this influence has been noted by some stockbreeders for many years it was not accepted as a fact by animal scientists until the so-called *Whitten phenomenon* was reported.

The Whitten phenomenon is one in which oestrus in mice can be synchronized and induced by the introduction of a male mouse into a colony of females. Carefully detailed experimental work on this phenomenon has established that the majority of the females come into oestrus as a result of being exposed to a specific odour from the male animal. There is evidence that this type of phenomenon may also occur among the various farm animals.

*Sheep.* It is known that the introduction of a ram to a flock of ewes can influence the commencement of the breeding season in that flock (Fig. 30). This effect can even be achieved without the ram having physical contact with the female members of the flock. Ram influence, being provided under practical conditions by 'teaser' rams, undoubtedly brings on seasonal breeding activities in ewes more rapidly than occurs when they are left in an all female

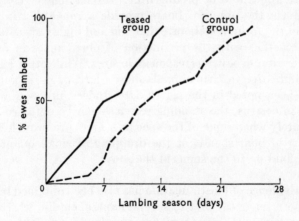

Fig. 30. The course of development of the lambing season in two groups of ewes in a flock of Suffolk sheep bred experimentally. One group was stimulated with a teaser ram for a period before natural breeding commenced.

group. The masculine stimulus may be provided visually by the sight or by the sound or odour of the ram. It would seem however that, whatever the stimulus, it can influence the breeding behaviour of ewes over some distance.

*Goats*. Very clear evidence of biostimulation has been observed in this animal. It has repeatedly been noted that the presence of a male goat in a herd of does has a stimulating effect on their breeding behaviour. This effect seems to occur after a latent period of 10 days following the introduction of the male animal to the female group so that synchronization of oestrus among the females is a characteristic of this biostimulation. The production of pheromones by male animals is suspected on circumstantial evidence in some species, for example in sheep; but the male goat produces characteristic odours which can even be detected by man over distances of hundreds of metres. There is, therefore, no doubt that pheromonal activity plays a part in goat breeding and behaviour.

*Pigs*. The production of pheromones by farm animals has been studied most intensively in the pig. It has been found that the boar produces a substance called muskone which appears to have the effect of prompting sows to display oestrous behaviour. This substance appears to be produced in a submaxilliary gland but is excreted via the prepuce. Boars provide a range of stimulating factors in the form of elaborate nudging and highly specific vocalization together with the production of pheromones in order to induce maximum oestrous responses in sows. While other examples of biostimulation in farm animals show a latency in response, this has not been noted in the pig to date. Indeed in a sow which is already in oestrus, the standing response can be obtained almost immediately when some of the specific stimuli are provided, e.g. a recording of boar sounds or the dropping of small quantities of seminal fluid on to the snout of the sow.

*Cattle*. Evidence of biostimulation has also been obtained in cattle. It has been reported, that in several experiments in which teaser bulls are run with groups of newly calved cows, the so-called teased animals show signs of oestrus much earlier than similar cows in control groups. Breeding behaviour may be shown 4 weeks earlier in the teased group than among controls. The phenomenon of biostimulation can play a considerable part in prompting breeding activities.

Oestrus can also be induced in many animals by genital stimulation in ways which resemble the Whitten phenomenon. Much of the scientific evidence pointing to the induction of oestrus by genital stimulation emerged very recently. There have been several reports of the induction of oestrus in cows and mares as a result of genital stimulation. Genital stimulation is normally supplied by male activity in the form of nuzzling, nudging and licking about the perineal region of the female animal. (This sort of behaviour in cattle was noted by cavemen fifteen thousand years ago.)

It is clear that the induction of oestrus in the farm animals is not only due to internal, endogenous factors but also to external, exogenous stimulation. The latter stimulation is complex involving odour, sound, sight and touch. Earlier it was supposed that oestrus was entirely under endogenous control, but it is clear now that exogenous factors are of considerable importance. The problem of anoestrus—the failure to show oestrus during the periods of the breeding season or life cycle when it should be shown—in farm animals might be attributed, in many cases, to the absence of exogenous factors through faulty husbandry.

# MATING

The farm animals have elaborate patterns of mating behaviour. These behaviour patterns are apparently concerned with stabilizing the mating relationships between the sexes. The mating patterns commence with cogent activities between the sexes which can be of variable duration and may extend into the period of mating proper. Although mating activities in farm animals are basically instinctive they are also partially learned. It is believed that the need for learning in mating behaviour is greater among male farm animals than females. Many livestock breeders complain about inadequacy of mating behaviour patterns in young boars and bulls. In these species some individuals require a lengthy learning process before competent mating behaviour emerges.

The principal component of mating behaviour is mounting. Mounting by both sexes is seen particularly in cattle. Mounting behaviour is also observed among very young animals which have by no means attained puberty and in this context it is simply play activity. In the sexually mature male, mounting behaviour becomes specifically orientated so that the female is appropriately covered for intromission to be effected. This directional aspect of mounting (taxis) again seems to be acquired by learning, but at the same time is shown more positively by male animals which are highly stimulated sexually. Disorientation both in the approach to mounting and in mounting itself are to be seen in male animals with a low level of libido whatever the cause. Male animals seldom mount the females of species other than their own, but stallions will mount female donkeys and jackasses will, likewise, mount mares—were this not so there would be no mules in the world. Occasionally sheep and goats will also intermate but normal pregnancies do not result. There have been reports of isolated instances of abnormal sexual behaviour in which the male of one species mounts oestrous females of a different species. They include bulls mounting mares and horses mounting heifers. In each of these cases the animals involved were stated to have been in each other's company continuously from early life.

So-called false mounting attempts by the male animal are commonly seen in the course of courtship. In these instances mounts apparently occur normally but dismounting subsequently follows quite quickly without any forelimb clasping or pelvic thrusting movements. False mounts show that the mechanics of mounting and of intromission are separately controlled. False mountings are to be seen in the mating patterns of the stallion, the sheep and the goat. In the stallion it is believed that some 2 or 3 false mounts are quite normal before effective mating is undertaken.

Following normal mounting, penile intromission is effected, but this is dependent on prior penile erection. Erection in the stallion is much less rapid than in the ruminants because of the muscular type of tissue of which the horse's penis is composed. This type of penis shows a delay in erection, and it may be for this reason that false mounts are customarily shown by stallions before mating takes place. The fibro-elastic structure of the penis in the bull and ram permits a more rapid erection and protrusion. The pig's penis is also of a similar type of tissue which erects and protrudes fairly rapidly. Penile erection in the boar is also associated with the development of a spiral in the terminal portion of the penis.

Intromission is effected following thrusting, seeking actions. In

Fig. 31. The progressive development of typical precoital activities
between a ram and oestrous ewe. (tracing)

Fig. 32.   Coital posture in the pig. Note spinal arc in the boar and ear
pricking in the sow. (tracing)

the ruminant species intromission consists only of a single pelvic
thrust which is followed by dismounting. In the stallion intromission is maintained for a period of a minute or more during
which there is pelvic thrusting and subsequently the adoption of a
fairly static posture after which dismounting occurs.

The manner of intromission in the pig (Fig. 32) is quite unique.
When the boar mounts he makes thrusting actions with the penis,
and the spiral tip of the penis shows semi-rotatory actions in
association with these thrusts. When intromission is effected the
spiral glans penis of the boar becomes tightly lodged in the firm
cervix of the sow. Only when the penis becomes lodged in this
fashion is proper intromission considered to be effected. Intromission is maintained once penile lodging has been effected and
during this time pelvic thrusting ceases. The duration of intromission averages about 9 minutes and during this time most boars
rest their heads and forefeet on the backs of sows. Stockmen refer
to this as treading. Indeed, following mating there are marks on
the sow's back indicating where the boar has 'treaded' with his
forefeet.

Among all the other farm animals mentioned there is positive
clasping by the male during intromission and mounting. The
stallion and the bull effect tight clasping of the respective female
with their forelegs abducted into her flanks. In the case of the

bull, this clasping increases in intensity at the moment of penetration and ejaculation. Vigorous clasping also takes place in mating between sheep but, when the male and female are heavily clad with wool, clasping is inevitably impaired to some degree. Recent studies suggest that more effective mating takes place when the female has been shorn before mating activities commence. If this is true then the explanation is likely to lie in improved clasping by rams in turn improving the ejaculatory process.

Following ejaculation male animals typically show a refractory period which is assumed to be a state of sexual exhaustion. The state of sexual exhaustion is not principally a physical one, however, and refers mainly to the loss of stimulus value by the female which has been mated. A quick return to mating behaviour is shown by male animals when they are given an opportunity to redirect their attention towards a new oestrous subject.

It is the normal procedure in mating among farm animals for repeated matings to occur with any given female. Stallions probably re-serve oestrous mares 5 to 10 times in each heat period and most rams are noted to remate with ewes 3 or 4 times. Bulls are seen to remate with oestrous cows repeatedly perhaps on 5 or 6 occasions. When running freely with breeding sows some boars have been reported to serve oestrous sows up to 11 times in one heat period. Male goats have also been noted to remate with does on 3 to 12 occasions during one oestrous period.

Variations occur in the degree of receptivity in oestrous female animals. Some studies have shown that many ewes permit about 6 matings during each heat period. When competition between ewes exist for a limited number of rams, it appears that older ewes are usually more successful than maiden ones in obtaining repeated matings.

A number of reports show that natural matings have the effect of shortening the duration of oestrus in horses and cattle. In one case it was reported that the period of receptivity in cattle was shortened by as much as 8 hours when natural circumstances were provided and repeated matings took place. These studies also show that, when female animals are 'teased' with vasectomized males prior to artificial insemination, they ovulate much more quickly than do unteased control animals. There is also increasing evidence that copulation shortens the duration of oestrus in all the farm animals compared with A.I.

Fig. 33.  Phases in equine courtship behaviour: (1) Greeting. (2) Interchange of sexual stimuli. (3) Oestrous display. (4) Female reception of male. (tracings)

# PAIRING BEHAVIOUR

Farm animals in free association often exhibit pairing behaviour in which the partners consort with each other in ways which are stereotyped for particular biological events. Such pairings can be termed bigeminal formations (Fig. 34). Although different formations may be observed in various activities such as suckling, grooming, social bonding and mating, specific geometric patterns are utilized in their expression. In these patterns the long axes of the partners are variously arranged in parallel positions and at angles of 90° or 180° to each other. The adoption of the bigeminal formation is a mutually designed manoeuvre.

The pairing which takes place most commonly between male and female farm animals is the previously described tending bond. It is apt to persist throughout most of the oestrous period of the female. The male is seldom swamped by association with other females to the extent of breaking these tending bonds before they

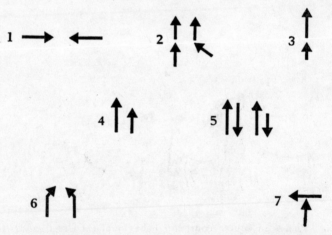

Fig. 34. Bigeminal Formations. A variety of paired formations are characteristically adopted in certain situations: (1) Preliminary social and agonistic exchanges. (2) Male alignment with oestrous females. (3) Neonate following dam after imprinting. (4) Dam and closely associating juvenile. (5) Parallel and opposite stances in tending bond and nursing. (6) Nosing between the sexes in precoital behaviour. (7) Dominance expression and precoital nudging.

have become fully established. One exceptional circumstance, however, occurs in the first few days of the breeding season among
sheep when large numbers of ewes may be in oestrus simultaneously.

When pairing has become established certain behavioural characteristics are frequently seen. Some of these are typical of individual
species but most species have certain positional arrangements in
common as part of their pairing behaviour. A common arrangement
is the one which has been described as the 'parallel and opposite'
position (Fig. 35) during which the two individuals stand side by side

Fig. 35.  The parallel and opposite bigeminal formation adopted by a
breeding pair of cattle during exhibition of the tending bond.
(tracing)

closely together and parallel, but facing in opposite directions. By
this means individuals maintain a fairly extensive lateral contact
with each other and this clearly affects the exchange of mutual
stimulation. Parallel and opposite stances have been noted frequently in cattle and in horses.

When a bull and cow have effected pairing bellowing between
the partners quickly subsides. The two animals spend a great deal
of time in mutual grooming which involves licking the hindquarters and the udder of the female and the prepuce, scrotum,
abdomen and flanks of the male. The necks and shoulders of both

Fig. 36.  The progressive development of precoital activities in a pair of breeding pigs. (tracing)

animals are included in these grooming activities. Pairings between stallions and mares show elements of behaviour which are characteristic of their species. In the early stages of precoitus, nose to nose contact is seen predominantly; following this the mare presents her hindquarters towards the stallion. The stallion pinches her working forwards from the flanks towards the shoulders. He also circles the oestrous mare from time to time with his head held low.

Many of the components of pairing behaviour can collectively be described as courtship activities. Courtship activities undoubtedly present themselves in behaviour patterns typical of particular species. In any one species the behaviour pattern of courtship consists of several phases which blend into each other in a specific chain of events. The principal behavioural features of courtship behaviour in sheep, horses and pigs are illustrated in Figs 31, 33 and 36 respectively. Some decades ago a very prominent animal scientist pronounced that, since oestrus was under physiological control in farm animals, no courtship behaviour was needed in these species and none was to be found. This belief was held by many for a considerable length of time. Today we can see how wrong it is, on all counts.

# SUPPLEMENTARY READING

BANE, A. (1954) Sexual functions of bulls in relation to heredity, rearing intensity and somatic conditions. *Acta Agric. scand.*, *4*, 95–208.

BANKS, E. M. (1964) Some aspects of sexual behaviour in domestic sheep, *Ovis aries. Behaviour, 23*, 249–279.

DESKUR, S. (1964) The first oestrus and ovulation after parturition in the mare. *Acta agrar. Silvest., Ser. zootech., 4*, 49–80. (*Anim. Breed. Abstr.* (1964), *33*, No. 3151).

DIMITROV, H., DRUGOCIU, G., DASCĂLU, A., LĂBUSCĂ, I. & POPESCU, N. (1959) Biostimulation of sexual processes of ewes. *Probleme zooteh. vet* (8), 51–54. (*Anim. Breed. Abstr.* (1961), *29*, No. 1501).

DONOVAN, B. J. & VAN DER WERFFSEN BOSCH, J. J. (1965) *Physiology of Puberty.* London: Edward Arnold.

FRASER, A. F. (1968) *Reproductive Behaviour in Ungulates.* London: Academic Press.

GLOD, W. (1961) Observations on the sexual cycle in cows, with special reference to oestrus and time of ovulation. *Medycyna wet., 17*, 353–361. (*Anim. Breed. Abstr.* (1962), *30*, No. 1723).

LAMONT, J. L. (1964) Influence of vasectomised bucks on the reproductive performance of Angora does. *S. Afr. J. agric. Sci., 7*, 305–310.

LINDSAY, D. R. (1965) The importance of olfactory stimuli in the mating behaviour of the ram. *Anim. Behav., 13*, 75–78.

PEPELKO, W. E. & CLEGG, M. J. (1965) Studies of the mating behaviour and some factors influencing the sexual response in the male sheep *Ovis aries. Anim. Behav., 13*, 249–258.

WHITTEN, W. K. (1956) Modification of the oestrous cycle of the mouse by external stimuli associated with the male. *J. Endocrin., 13*, 399–404.

# 11.

# Fetal Behaviour

CAVE drawings show that very early man was aware that fetuses were carried inside the body of the animals that were his prey (Fig. 37). His drawings also show that he realized that the fetuses possessed eyes and ears, for these sense organs have been depicted in a functionally accurate way. Altogether it is not unreasonable to suppose that cave man was aware of fetal life, though even today

Fig. 37.   Cave drawing of one animal within another—believed by archaeologists to represent an attempt at depicting a fetus. (copy)

our awareness of fetal activity still remains comparatively slight and inaccurate. Embryology has been so concerned with the developmental and morphological aspects of the fetus that the subject of behaviour has virtually been neglected. Indeed, it is impossible to refer students of farm animal behaviour to any publication providing adequate information on fetal behaviour. Fetuses, nevertheless, are markedly involved in a variety of behavioural activities.

# GENERAL ACTIVITY OF THE FETUS

At an early stage in development, towards the end of the first one-third of its gestation period, the fetus starts to engage in phases of vigorous bodily movement within the amniotic bladder. These movements involve jerking of the major body parts, the limbs in particular. By ultrasonic examination of farm animal fetuses it has been possible to detect fetal life in the form of heartbeats and fetal movement at this stage. The apparatus used for this purpose directs an ultrasonic beam into the abdomen of a pregnant animal. Any movement cutting into this ray of ultrasound causes a change in sonic frequency which is reflected back to the instrument as a change in pitch. This change in pitch caused by a moving object is referred to as the Doppler phenomenon.

Recent research on the Doppler phenomenon in farm animal fetuses has added important items of information to our knowledge of fetal life. The fetal heart can be detected beating regularly and strongly from an age of several weeks, and erratic fetal movements can be detected almost as soon as the heart develops its pulsating action. General fetal movements have been detected as early as 2 months of gestation in mares, 7 weeks of gestation in cows, 9 weeks in sheep and 6 weeks in pigs. Fetal movements are sudden and sharp, and cut across the ultrasonic reflection from the fetal heart so as to superimpose their own signal on the recording. Fetal activities of this nature usually last only a few seconds. These brief bursts of activity are repeated frequently, usually in quick succession. The phases of activity are spaced throughout the day, and current observations suggest that they take place scores of times daily in the middle period of gestation in all the farm animals. Fetal activity becomes increasingly evident with the progression of gestation; this has been noted particularly in pig fetuses. In the later stages of gestation in pigs fetal activity appears to involve large numbers of fetuses collectively, suggesting that in this species fetal activity resembles an 'all or none' phenomenon.

These phases of activity are interspersed with periods during which the fetus is apparently dormant. From this picture of alternating activity and inactivity, a concept of the general pattern of fetal behaviour can be built up. A recording of one typical spasm

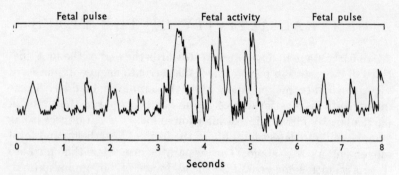

Fig. 38. Spasms of fetal activity detected by Doppler ultrasound in a 12-week sheep fetus.

of fetal activity is shown in Fig. 38. Fetal actions of this kind become more sluggish but more powerful in the prepartum period, and it is suggested that at this time the righting reflexes of the fetus are being undertaken preparatory to the birth process.

Observant horse breeders have noted marked fetal activity, amounting almost to a 'turbulence', beneath the flanks of mares in the 24 hours preceding foaling.

# POSITIONAL FETAL BEHAVIOUR

## *Polarity and Rotation*

In one preliminary research project on this problem, studies were made on the gestational movement of the bovine fetus in relation to its presentation at birth. In these studies it became evident that the final presentation of the fetus at birth does not arise during parturition but exists from an earlier time in gestation. The research showed that during the first 2 months of gestation in cattle no definite polarity of the fetus could be found, but in the third month there was evidence of a tendency towards a longitudinal presentation with an equal number of fetuses being disposed anteriorly and posteriorly. Throughout the fourth, fifth and sixth months of the 9-month gestation the majority of bovine fetuses were in posterior presentation, but towards the end of the sixth month the majority of fetuses adopted an anterior presentation. After the seventh month only 6% of the fetuses had failed to turn to an anterior position—a situation that prevailed right up until fullterm. It is clear, therefore, that the polarity of the bovine fetus becomes reversed from posterior to anterior at about the fifth to sixth month of gestation. In these studies it was assumed that this change in fetal polarity could only be effected by fetal movements occurring in responses to intra-uterine pressure, the change in pressure probably being the result of increased uterine muscle tone. The researchers were of the opinion that those fetuses which failed to reverse their polarity at the critical time were less well developed, particularly in their nervous systems.

In the final stages of gestation the typical posture of the bovine fetus is one of anterior presentation in the dorsal position. In contrast the equine fetus is normally in an upside-down position right up to the termination of pregnancy, at which time the fetus must undertake its own rotational correction before birth can be effected.

## *Fetal Righting Reflexes*

The posture of general flexion becomes changed in the week prior to birth when the first righting reflexes are taking effect. It is difficult to be exact about the time at which these righting reflexes first take place in the different species. It is likely that in the foal fetus they first occur about 1 to 2 weeks before the end of gestation. The point when righting reflexes appear to commence in cattle is about a week before birth, and in pigs and sheep 3 to 5 days beforehand.

Limb kicking by the fetus becomes much more powerful at this time, and one of its effects is to put the fetus into a more extended posture than earlier in pregnancy. During gestation it is usual for the fetus to have its head and limbs flexed, but in the immediate prepartum period these parts assume an extended posture. This change in posture is, of course, necessary to facilitate birth.

Although farm animals normally give birth to fetuses with the fore-end protruding first, about 15% of fetuses are born hind-end first. Providing that the feet precede the head or the rump respectively, both the anterior and the posterior form of presentation can be considered normal.

Stretching and full extension by the fetus are required before the uterine contractions proceed to the point where the fetus is driven part of the way down the birth canal. Uterine contractions occur for many hours before the birth process proper commences, and this contraction downwards on to it gives the fetus firm support all around it making its righting reflexes more effective. When these reflexes are not effective, a difficult parturition is virtually inevitable. Dystocia is more often the result of this set of circumstances than any other.

In a study of 457 cases of dystocia in sheep in one year it was found that the majority of these were associated with malpresentation of the fetus. Most malpresentations involved the delivery of the fetus fore-end first, but with one or both forelegs being retained. The proportion of cases in which the head was turned back was relatively small. About one-third of all difficult births were due to the retention of one or both of the forelimbs. Clearly, in these cases, the fetuses had been unable to alter their limbs from the flexed position of gestation to one of extension.

If, as a result of an unsatisfactory fetal posture at the time of birth, the birth process is delayed it is likely that many fetuses involved in dystocia will have their oxygen supply impaired before they are born properly and able to breathe. Intra-natal anoxic episodes are now more widely recognized among farm animals, foals in particular, and the consequences of these episodes are seen to be serious. A fetus which suffers an anoxic episode at the time of birth will almost certainly have some severe impairment, such as damage to the central nervous system. These newborn creatures are frequently found to be incapable of adapting to their new post-parturient environments. The problems of fetal dystocia and neonatal insufficiency are considerable, and they must in many cases be linked with features of fetal life prepartum.

The righting reflexes in the fetus, like many other forms of behaviour, have a genetic basis and therefore can show some breed and species variation. It is recognizable now that the precise time at which gestation becomes terminated is very largely controlled by hormonal changes in the fetus. If these changes marginally affect the length of gestation that is typical of a given breed of ewe, then early or late births may result. For example, it has been found that Cheviot ewes have an average gestation of 150 days with pure bred fetuses and one of 146·5 days with cross-Finnish Landrace fetuses. Dystocia is not infrequently associated with abnormal gestation lengths. When gestation is protracted, it is likely that further fetal development will result in excessive size and consequential difficulty in birth. On the other hand, if the fetus has a slightly shorter gestation than normal, it may be born before righting reflexes have properly been effected. If the fetus is small, an abnormal posture may not create an insurmountable difficulty to birth, but if it is physically well developed and has failed to complete its righting reflexes satisfactorily, dystocia will result.

It is considered that this fact is the cause of many of the birth problems in the ewe. As previously mentioned, the majority of difficult births involve uncompleted righting reflexes prior to birth. Different breeds of sheep have different lengths of gestation, and it may well be that the common practice of cross-breeding sheep leads to fetuses which do not have their righting reflexes timed to correspond with the resulting gestation periods.

## INGESTIVE AND ELIMINATIVE FETAL BEHAVIOUR

From a very early age the fetus eliminates urine through its urachus into its amniotic bladder. This becomes diluted in the amniotic fluids in which the fetus is suspended. From an early age, also, the fetus undertakes swallowing reflexes in the course of which the same amniotic fluid is ingested. This form of ingestive activity becomes increasingly common in the later stages of gestation. Indeed, towards the terminal part of gestation, the fetus is ingesting large quantities of amniotic fluid; the quantities of fluid consumed at this time greatly exceed its own body weight. As a consequence of this ingestion the alimentary canal of the fetus accumulates residue of a solid nature.

The accumulation of residue in the alimentary canal progresses until the rectum also becomes filled. It is unusual for the fetus to defaecate even though, by the end of gestation, the rectum is almost certain to be full of meconium (or fetal faeces). However, there is a limit to the length of time that a fetus can retain this meconium in its rectum; if its bodily maturation progresses beyond a certain point then defaecation may occur before birth.

If the fetus suffers stress during the birth processes, fetal defaecation is also usually evident. The stress in the fetus may be a result of continuous and excessive pressures from the contracting uterus.

It is also conceivable that the fetus should share in any stress experienced by the dam during the parturient process. Certainly it has been observed that the fetal heart rate accelerates markedly at a time when the dam is being handled forcefully in the course of some management procedure. In one such case, it was noted that the fetal pulse increased from 180 per minute to over 300 per minute. This increase in pulse rate developed fairly quickly and was maintained for a period of several minutes before it decelerated to its previous rate. During this time the dam was vigorously fighting against the manual control to which she was being subjected. Fetuses therefore evidently can suffer stress.

It is commonly noted that when adult cattle are suddenly disturbed they undergo reflex defaecation in response; it would appear that the fetus shows a similar response to circumstances in which it is stressed. As a result of defaecation into its amniotic fluids the fetus itself becomes tinted with characteristic meconium staining, viz. an orange to ochre colouring. Meconium staining is an indication that the fetus, at the time of birth, has either attained a very advanced stage of maturation or, alternatively, has experienced some stress prior to parturition being completed.

If the length of coat on a newborn animal is some indication of maturity it would seem that the newborn lamb is the most mature of all the farm animal neonates. Thus it is not surprising to observe that a large number of lambs do have meconium staining on them following birth. It would be unwise, therefore, to assume that meconium staining on the newborn animal is invariably an indication that the subject has experienced prior stress.

## SUPPLEMENTARY READING

ARTHUR, G. H. (1966) Recent advances in bovine obstetrics. *Vet. Rec.*, *79*, (22), 630–640.

FRASER, A. F., KEITH, N. W. & HASTIE, H. (1973) Summarised observations on the ultrasonic detection of pregnancy and fetal life in the mare. *Vet. Rec.*, *92*, 20–21.

# 12.

# Parturition

PARTURIENT behaviour is characterized by a series of connected episodes. These developments collectively make up the process of 'before, during and after' birth. This process has been documented comprehensively in relatively few species, because parturition is of quite brief and rare occurrence in comparison with many other animal activities. The observation and recording of parturition can only be made on individual animals and over a prolonged period of time.

Many free-living species seek out remote or concealed sites for giving birth, and there are also strong indications that many domesticated animals deliberately try to avoid the hours of supervision when allowing the birth process to take place. However, because they can be kept under close supervision, the behaviour of farm animals during parturition is relatively well explored.

## THE PHASES OF PARTURITION

The process of birth passes through three very definite stages; this is normally the case with species in which single births occur. But in those animals in which multiple births occur (pigs for example) it can be said that there are only two phases, the second and third stages being interchanged regularly. The first stage refers to the dilation of the cervix and the associated behaviour of the animal. The second stage is the expulsion of the fetus itself. The third stage is the passage of the afterbirth of fetal membranes. These phases extend into the broader, more general behavioural periods of prepartum, birth and postpartum.

### The Pre-parturient Period

The pre-parturient period extends from late gestation (the carrying of the unborn fetus by the mother) to the beginning of the first stage of labour. Apart from certain changes in attitude towards

135

any previous offspring still being nursed, there is generally little of significance in the animals' behaviour until parturition itself is very close. Once parturition is imminent, many animals separate themselves from the main group and select a site for the birth. Many species at free range choose inaccessible areas where the birth may occur unhindered. The domesticated ruminants often appear to withdraw from the grazing group when birth is only an hour or two away but, in some of these cases, the parturient animal has simply failed to keep up with the grazing drift of the main herd or flock.

It has been observed in the pre-parturient sow that, while most of the time during the 3 days before the onset of labour is spent sleeping and feeding, an increasing amount of nest-building behaviour is shown. This is usually evident in the form of bedding chopping. In the immediate prepartum phase (the 24 hours before farrowing) definite behaviour patterns begin to emerge. The animal becomes increasingly restless and frequently alters her position and possibly also her disposition. Gradually still greater restlessness becomes evident until a stage is reached where the animal changes her position every few minutes. Recognition of this preparturient behaviour in the pregnant animal allows the time of birth to be predicted accurately in the great majority of cases. Forewarning such as this allows the corrective husbandry of parturient animals and their neonates. A similar pattern of behaviour to that in the parturient sow is seen in the cow: much sleeping and feeding during the days immediately before parturition and moments of restlessness culminating in almost continuously restless and erratic behaviour. Sometimes, during the pre-parturient period, muscular contractions of the kind that herald the onset of labour itself may even take place so that one is given the impression that the actual birth is about to occur. There is strong behavioural evidence of the buildup of pain in the parturient animal during the late prepartum phase. The biological evidence of this pain in mares, cows and ewes has been considered extensively, and it seems that the pain serves to signal the forthcoming events to the animal. Pain secures the entire attention of the parturient animal and its total participation in the birth process. Increasing restlessness and other evidence of a buildup of pain constitute the predominant indications of the late prepartum period and the phase associated with the first stage of labour.

## *Birth*

Pain is most evident during the phase which corresponds with the second stage of labour, i.e. birth.

As has been noted, the activities of the single-bearing (monotocous) dam are separable into three phases. In the multiple-bearing (polytocous) species, the parturient process is such that the activities of the second and third stages are interrelated; the two stages being interchanged at fairly regular intervals. It would be more accurate therefore to talk of only two stages, namely, the preparturient period and the period of fetus and fetal membrane expulsion.

With the effacement of the cervix on completion of the first stage, the contents of the uterus can move through the open birth canal and invade the vagina. After the uterine contents have passed through the fully opened cervix the next phase of the birth can begin.

The outer fetal membrane (the chorion) remains adherent to the uterine wall and, during the course of physical straining, becomes rent with pressure. This allows the amniotic bladder containing the fetus to bulge the vagina—which is lined with secretions of cervical mucus and chorionic fluid—and effects further dilatation so that the fetus enters the pelvic canal. At this stage of labour the contractions of the uterus are regular. Even at the end of this stage, they can be very strong and frequent. These events terminate the second stage with an acceleration in the expulsive efforts of the dam. Provided there is no impediment to its delivery, the fetus is then expelled by a combination of voluntary and involuntary muscular contractions in the abdomen and uterus. Repeated straining (particularly abdominal straining) is therefore the principal feature of maternal behaviour at birth. The manner and degree of straining varies from one species to another as does also the behaviour during the other parturient phases. Individual behavioural characteristics of some of the domestic species are given separate mention later in this chapter, but some valid generalizations are given below.

The straining efforts increase in number and recur more regularly when the second stage of labour has begun. At this time the strong reflex abdominal and diaphragmatic contractions are synchronized with those of the uterus. The straining sessions are punctuated by resting intervals each lasting a few minutes. Further extrusion of the fetus is not necessarily achieved with each straining bout. The course of extrusion is subject to arrest and even retraction of the fetus back into the dam. One of the main obstacles to single births is the passage of the fetal forehead through the taut rim of the dam's vulvar opening. Once the head is born the rate of passage of the fetus is greatly accelerated. The shoulders follow the head within a few minutes and, immediately after this, the remainder of the neonate very quickly slips out of the birth passage. The mother's vigorous straining usually ceases when the fetal trunk has been born; often there is a short resting period at this point while the hind limbs of the neonate are still in the recumbent mother's pelvis (an event commonly occurring in unassisted horse births). Immediately on being born, ungulate neonates exhibit typical struggling leg movements and upward tilting of the face before they make efforts to stand. These movements are collective groups of 'righting' reflexes.

During birth, the posture of the dam varies a great deal. In some species the dam remains recumbent throughout birth; in others there is alternate lying, standing and crouching. The duration of the second stage of labour is usually much shorter than the first stage.

## The Post-parturient Period

In the immediate postpartum period, the dam is engaged in the third stage of labour and in the grooming of the neonate. The third stage is mainly concerned with the expulsion of the fetal membranes or afterbirth. There is not normally any vigorous straining during the expulsion of the membranes after their internal dehiscence. Fetal membranes are usually passed fairly effortlessly by the dam during the first few hours following the birth. Many animals occupy themselves by eating the afterbirth after its final expulsion (placentophagia). It has been said by some observers that the time thus spent by the mother parallels the efforts of the newborn in struggling and attempting to mobilize itself. Not all animals are placentophagic; cows and sows are, while mares are not. It seems that the two groups do have certain general behavioural characteristics which differ. The species that are placentophagic usually keep their newborn close to the birth site for several days at least, whilst those that are not lead their sucklings away from the birth site very early on in the post-parturient period. It has been noted that in natural circumstances mares foal at night and in the open so that, by daybreak, the foals can trot and have been led away by their mothers. It does seem however that the instinct for placentophagy has been modified significantly in domesticated species. Some individual pigs and cattle show it to a well-developed degree while others, of the same species, do not. There appears to be no nutritional value attached to the consumption of the afterbirths; they have been found in undigested form in the bovine rumen 2 weeks after their ingestion. It may be concluded that the placentophagy is a facet of the maternal instinct to protect the vulnerable neonate.

Immediately postpartum the grooming and nursing of the newborn begin. During the critical first few post-parturient hours, the mother and the newborn learn to recognize each other through a series of visual, auditory, olfactory, gustatory and tactile clues. This mutual recognition forms the basis of the social attachment which typifies the behavioural responses of dam and offspring to each other.

## SPECIES-SPECIFIC PARTURIENT BEHAVIOUR

Detailed parturient events, typical of the various farm animal species, are given below.

### The Mare

The first indications that a mare is near foaling can be seen in the swelling of the udder and teats which, in most cases, becomes apparent about 2 days before the birth occurs. Also at this time, a wax-like fluid is emitted from the teats; although this may occur weeks before actual foaling. About 4 hours before parturition sweating is evident at the elbows and on the flanks. The first sign of labour occurs when the mare becomes increasingly restless. She may perform circling movements, look round at her flanks, get up and lie down spasmodically and generally show signs of anxiety.

At the onset of parturition feeding ceases abruptly. The mare rises and lies down again more frequently than before, rolls on the ground and slaps her tail against her perineum. Subsequently she adopts a characteristic straddling position and crouching posture frequently urinating at the same time. The mare may also show flehmen, especially after the allantoic fluid has escaped with the rupture of the allantochorion about the end of the first stage of labour when extremely vigorous straining—typical of the mare alone—occurs for the first time.

Just before straining starts, an unusually high raising of the head is sometimes observed. But when straining begins the mare soon goes down flat on her side and the expulsive efforts become intensified. From the first signs of sweating it may be deduced that the first stage of labour which lasts for about 4 hours has begun, but false starts are not uncommon. After some straining the waterbag (amniotic sac) becomes extruded; within it one fetal foot usually precedes the other. The bouts of straining become more and more vigorous until the muzzle of the fetus appears above the fetlocks. (Although the straining bouts at this period are very vigorous the amniotic sac does not rupture.) Most of the delivery time is normally taken up with the birth of the foal's head. Soon after this the remainder of the foal, except its hind feet, is expelled from the vagina. The reflex head movements of the almost wholly born foal finally burst the amniotic sac; the foal begins to breathe and its further reflex limb actions may extract the remainder of its hind legs from the dam. Final expulsion of the legs may be caused by the mare rising.

The duration of this second stage of labour is, on average, about 17 minutes although in normal circumstances it may last anything from 10 to 70 minutes. Following the completion of birth mares often lie, in apparent exhaustion, for 20 to 30 minutes. As has previously been stated, mares do not eat their afterbirths although they do groom their foals. The usual length of time for the third stage is about 1 hour, and following the extrusion of the fetal membranes the foal engages in suckling within an hour and begins to trot after about 4 hours. Mares generally foal at night and in the open if possible. The mare will often teach the foal to trot by herself, trotting around the foal in a circular manner.

Parturition

# The Cow

Until the first stage of labour has begun physical changes rather than behavioural ones are apparent in the pre-parturient cow. Ingestive behaviour is, however, reduced at the time that labour is about to start. It is also at this time that the animal begins to show regular periods of restlessness; feeding sometimes recommences between these periods. Eventually the restlessness gives way to behaviour which is very similar to that encountered in conditions of colic. The cow appears apprehensive, looking all round her and turning her ears in various directions for brief periods. At this period the cow will also perambulate excessively if she is at all able. She will also occasionally examine patches of ground and sometimes even paw loose litter or bedding as though gathering it into one spot.

The first stage of labour becomes apparent when the cow goes through the motions of lying down and getting up again. She may also kick at her abdomen, repeatedly tread with her hind feet and look around to her flanks, and shift her position frequently. About this time, also, the cow begins to pass small amounts of faeces and urine at intervals while arching her back and straining slightly. Cows tend to show these bouts of slight straining earlier on in parturition than the other farm species. With time, the spasms of evident pain become better defined and more frequent. Finally they begin to appear regularly about every quarter of an hour and each spasm lasts about 20 seconds. The spasms are manifested by several straining actions in quick succession. After some bouts of straining, the allantochorion or first waterbag is rent and a straw-coloured urine-like fluid escapes. After this there is usually a short pause in the straining and muscular contractions. This pause terminates the first stage of labour which may vary in duration from 3 hours to 2 days, though a period of 4 hours is a more common (modal) average time.

About 1 hour later the more powerful straining of the second stage of labour becomes evident and the amnion appears at the vulva. This time, straining occurs about every 3 minutes and lasts for about half a minute but grows more powerful and more frequent when portions of the calf, such as its forefeet, become extruded at the vulva. At this stage the cow either adopts the normal resting position or lies on her side. Her upper legs may even swing clear of the ground if she strains while lying flat on her side. Straining is virtually continuous until the head and trunk of the calf extrudes. With the birth of the anterior part of the calf most cows quickly rise to a standing position and the remainder of the calf (the hindquarters) slips from the pelvis, and the birth is completed with the breakage of the umbilical cord. Occasionally a cow rising after the main period of extrusion will do so with the pelvis of the calf still lodged inside her own, and the retained fetus may swing from her for a period of time before dropping to the ground quite unharmed. Second stage labour, i.e. birth, is usually completed within an hour.

The cow often licks up her uterine discharges before the birth is completed. Once the calf is born, she rests for a variable length of time and then gets up and licks the fetal membranes and fluids from the calf. She usually eats the placenta and sometimes the bedding contaminated by fetal and placental fluids as well. Thus for a very short while the normally herbivorous creature becomes carnivorous.

The neonate calf attempts to stand soon after birth and quickly gains control over its legs and becomes able to walk. It is at about this time that the grooming and nursing of the neonate becomes intensified. Immediately postpartum, the mother and calf remain close together. Tactile stimulation of the udder during suckling helps to facilitate milk let-down as the calf feeds for the first time. The neonate spends most of its time postpartum grazing while the mother rests when the young is not suckling. After a day or two the free range cow returns to the herd with her young, and gradually the calf becomes increasingly integrated with the herd and less attached to the mother.

## The Sow

Prominent features in the pre-parturient sow include intermittent grunting, champing of the jaws and rapid breathing. There is also a significant enlargement of the mammary glands. During the 24-hour period before parturition nest-building also takes place. This activity may start up to 3 days before parturition. The nature of these nest-building activities may, however, largely depend on the material that she is provided with. The sow will attempt to clean and dry her selected birth site and will chew long grass or straw to provide bedding, carrying it a considerable distance if necessary. The location of the prospective birth site may be changed more than once. Pawing activities are evident where the sow uses her forelegs to move the bedding about. In general sows adopt and maintain a lying posture at rest before birth. It has been observed that free-living sows like to find a wooded area to build a den with dry vegetation. The dens are lined with chewed-up undergrowth and leaves, and the site of the birth place is dry and warm, as far as possible. In a concrete pen the sow will still satisfy her nesting tendencies using any material that is provided for her use. She will often resist human attempts to disturb or relocate her nest. The amount of time taken over the building of a nest varies from one sow to another but they nearly all make use of the straw, hay and any other dry material that is at hand.

During the process of delivery the sow is normally recumbent and lies on her side, although there are occasions when some sows adopt a position of ventral recumbency (lying on the sternum). Vigorous movements of the sow's tail herald each birth and the piglets are expelled without a great deal of evident difficulty. Although as has been stated polytocous species more accurately exhibit only two stages of parturition, relatively little afterbirth is passed until all the piglets are born.

When farrowing is only a few hours away the sow alternately utters soft grunting noises and shrill whining sounds. As parturition approaches she begins to grunt more intensely and emits loud squeals. Farrowing more often occurs during the night than at any other time. During farrowing, the recumbent sow may occasionally try to stretch out and kick with the upper hind leg or turn over on to her other side. These movements force out fluids and a fetus may be expelled at this time. Sometimes, during the birth of a piglet, the sow's body trembles and if she is of nervous temperament she may emit grunting and squealing noises. Piglets are expelled at an average rate of one every 15 minutes. Nervous sows often stand up after the birth of each piglet; this may be associated with temporary reduction in pressure in the reproductive tract. The entire farrowing process normally lasts about 3 hours. The umbilical cord of the piglet is unbroken at birth and remains so until the piglet can break free of the vulval flaps and move about. Piglets become mobile soon after birth. The sow pays little attention to her young until the last one is born and, when finally she rises, she sometimes voids quantities of urine.

The fetal membranes are expelled in batches of two to four after all the piglets have been born although some small portion is often passed during the birth process. Many sows will eat all or a part of the expelled afterbirth unless it is removed immediately.

Following parturition she will often call her litter to suck by emitting repeated short grunts, and may emit loud barking grunts if an intruder disturbs the nest. The sow rarely licks or grooms her young but sometimes appears to try to position the piglets near her udder or draw them towards her teats using her fore legs in scooping actions.

It is important to provide close observation over a particularly nervous sow for it is in such an animal that cannibalism is most likely to occur. With such a sow also, the young are sometimes crushed by sudden and erratic movements. The piglets can be removed immediately after birth if the sow shows signs of dystocia. After the process is over and her piglets are returned she will usually display normal responses towards them.

## The Ewe

It has commonly been observed that the ewe develops a premature maternal instinct. This is evident when the parturient ewe shows increasing interest in the lambs of other ewes. Occasionally ewes, evidently provoked by a particularly strong maternal drive, will attempt to take possession of other ewes' lambs (see Fig. 55, p. 182) and will sometimes do so successfully. It has been observed that well-fed ewes in good physical condition are especially susceptible to this tendency; more so than sheep in poorer physical condition which would more likely characterize pregnant sheep under natural, undomesticated conditions.

Recent studies of the behaviour of parturient ewes have been made with a particular view to investigating the temporal aspects. The onset of parturition was first signalled in about 50% of ewes through physical signs: the protrusion of the amniotic sac and part of the fetus, the release of amniotic fluid and the passing of bloody mucus. In another 33% of cases, behavioural signs were at first more evident than physical ones. All the characteristic behavioural signs, even when they did not constitute evidence of impending parturition, were noted. Although no clear pattern was found, a picture has emerged in which the behavioural pattern of parturient pain is clearly evident. A small number of ewes separate themselves from the main flock when parturition is imminent. Most ewes display signs of nervous and restless behaviour: lying down and getting up again, paddling with the hind feet and other classic signs of discomfort. In 17% of ewes no initial signs of parturition were evident at all, although the sheep were kept under close supervision and almost constant observation at the appropriate times during two lambing seasons.

Although there may be frequent lying down and rising before birth most ewes remain recumbent until the fetus is partially or completely expelled. In cases of twin and multiple births the neonates usually follow each other within a matter of minutes.

The mean joint duration of the first and second stages of labour is 80 minutes. The process of parturition in ewes would therefore normally seem to be a fairly swift one. The standard deviation in time of lamb delivery is about 50 minutes and the lambing times would follow the normal distribution were it not for cases of parturition of over 22 hours due to difficulty in birth (dystocia). There is no apparent difference in duration between breeds or ages. Although ewes lamb at all times during the 24-hour period, it has been observed over a period of time covering several lambing seasons that an unusual and disproportionately large number of ewes lamb during the 4-hour period lasting from 7 pm until 11 pm and also during the early morning hours from 5 am until 9 am.

Ewes chew and eat parts of the fetal membranes but they do not consume the entire afterbirth.

## The Doe Goat

The development of parturition in does and ewes is fairly similar. Immediately after the birth, the maternal orientation of the neonate allows the doe to administer further, more intensive, grooming of the young. Mutual recognition by the dam and the neonate is important in this animal (and also in ewes). A doe will often reject her kid if it is taken away immediately after birth and returned after a lapse of time. In some cases it has been known for does to reject the young kid after only 1 hour of absence following parturition. This subject is dealt with under the maternal drive and its manifestations (see pp. 24–25, 139). The drive is mentioned here however since its mainspring lies in parturition.

## THE TIMING OF PARTURITION

There are logical reasons for assuming that parturition, even when it seems to be imminent, can be postponed by an animal if there is no immediately suitable birth site or if the onset of labour comes at a time of disturbance or supervision.

It is an established fact that more births take place in farm animals during the hours of darkness than at any other time. Over 80% of mares foal at night, for example, and evidence suggests that they may be capable of delaying parturition if they deem it necessary. Although it is accepted that sheep lamb at all times during the 24-hour period, an unusual number of ewes give birth in the early hours of darkness. More cows also calve in the night than during the day. However, this delaying activity cannot continue indefinitely; once the physiological processes of labour have progressed to a certain stage, the animal is no longer capable of postponing parturition.

At the onset of labour, oxytocin is the dominant influence. The actions of oxytocin can be blocked by adrenaline and it is known that adrenaline is freely produced in the roused subject. Thus it may be concluded that an animal can control or delay parturition in the initial stages by adrenaline secretion; however this is not always true and in any case the postponement can only be temporary.

Parturient synchronization points to a form of maternal protection which may be either conscious or unconscious. For example, it has been found that many mares foal during the early summer when nutrition is at its height.

Mares mated early on in the breeding season will often foal at the same time as those which mate later on in the season. Apart from this synchronizing effect on gestation, it has been found that seasonal factors may also affect the time of birth. Comparing two groups of mares, it was found that the average length of time of gestation was 8 days longer in those which foaled in the spring than those which foaled in the autumn. A similar pattern in gestation has been found in other animals and it has been suggested that this behaviour could point to an 'inner timing' mechanism.

An aspect of parturient behaviour which effects protection for neonates as a group is the concentration of births during a particular time. The neonate, which is vulnerable to many predators, has a greater chance of survival where the sheer number of young born together leaves the predator with a material glut which lasts only for a short time. The birth times of lambs are synchronized to a degree; this is most evident in hill breeds. It has also been found in a herd of Angora does that, during one season, two-thirds of the kids were born within a 4-day period.

# SUPPLEMENTARY READING

ARTHUR, G. H. (1961) Some observations on the behaviour of parturient farm animals with particular reference to cattle. *Vet. Rev. May & Baker, 12*, 75–84.

CLEGG, M. J. (1959) Factors affecting gestation length and parturition. In: *Reproduction in Domestic Animals*, ed. H. H. Cole & P. J. Cupps, vol. 1, chapter 15. New York: Academic Press.

CROSS, B. A. (1959) Neurohypophyseal control of parturition. In: *Recent Progress in the Endocrinology of Reproduction*, ed. C. W. Lloyd, pp. 441–453. New York: Academic Press.

HINDSON, J. C., SCHOFIELD, B. M., TURNER, C. B. & WOLFF, H. S. (1965) Parturition in the sheep. *J. Physiol., Lond., 181*, 560–567.

JONES, J. E. T. (1966) Parturition in the sow: Part 1 The pre-partum phase. Part II The parturient and post-parturient phases. *Br. vet. J., 122*, 420–426, 471–478.

LINDAHL, J. L. (1964) Time of parturition in ewes. *Anim. Behav., 12*, 231–234.

ROSSDALE, P. D. & SHORT, R. V. (1967) The time of foaling of thoroughbred mares. *J. Reprod. Fert., 13*, 341–343.

SMITH, F. V. (1965) Instinct and learning in the attachment of lamb and ewe. *Anim. Behav., 13*, 84–86.

SMITH, F. V., VAN-TOLLER, C. & BOYES, T. (1966) The 'critical period' in the attachment of lambs and ewes. *Anim. Behav., 14*, 120–125.

WALSER, K. (1965) Über den Geburtsschmerz bei Tieren. *Tierärztl. Wschr., 78* (17), 321–324.

# 13.

# Neonatal Behaviour

## NURSING

Nursing—the active feeding relationship between neonate and mother—is promoted by the seeking and massaging activities of the newborn which are directed towards the udder. Experiments have shown that newborn animals show a distinct preference for soft objects and this may in part account for the motivation towards the udder.

*Horses.* Soon after the foal is born it attempts shakily to rise to its feet while being licked and nosed by the dam. Once it is able

Fig. 39.  Parallel axis in equine nursing formation with **mare** nosing foal's posterior pole. (tracing)

148

to move steadily, its activities are directed towards locating the mare's teats. At this point the foal may also attempt to nuzzle nearby inanimate objects or parts of the mare's body, often making teat-seeking attempts in the dam's pectoral region. The newborn animal is pushed and nosed by the dam in the general direction of her udder and is also assisted by strategic maternal manoeuvring. Once the udder has been located the foal selects one of the teats and sucks. Once the foal has grasped the teat it wraps its tongue around it and the resultant pressure stimulates the onset of milk-flow.

The newborn foal is normally able to engage in efficient suckling within 2 hours of parturition.

As with ruminant species which also suckle in the standing position, the newborn foal's teat-seeking activities are initially directed at the underside of the dam. This anatomical feature serves as a releaser for this behaviour.

With teat-seeking behaviour accomplished, the neonate sucks at the udder whilst keeping its long axis in a parallel and opposite position to the mare (Fig. 39). This attitude has the effect of presenting the foal's hindquarters towards the mare's head. In adopting this attitude the foal has to rotate its neck and extend its head into the mare's inguinal region (Fig. 40). This cervical rotation is a special feature of equine nursing. Foals continue to adopt this posture without modification during their nursing activities right up to weaning.

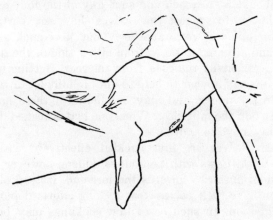

Fig. 40.   Head tilting and neck twisting in a young nursing foal. (tracing)

149

Fig. 41.  Initial teat-seeking activity in a newborn calf. (tracing)

*Cattle*. When the calf is able to stand after birth and moves towards the dam, its attention is directed towards the underside of the cow (Fig. 41) and ultimately the udder. The dam licks the calf during its teat-seeking possibly to stimulate and reinforce these neonatal activities and also to promote urination or defaecation by the calf.

The neonate calf bends its neck downwards, tilting its head upwards to grasp the teat. It is possible for the animal, by depressing its shoulders, to reach and suck any of the four teats. There is no evidence to suggest that calves show any particular preference for one teat over another. They may suck any teat at random and are able to do so from either side of the dam's body or, as is occasionally the case, from the rear. Butting movements made by the calf appear to help to initiate milk let-down and ease tension in the udder, and may be elicited if there has been an interruption in the milk-flow. When one teat is sucked dry the calf will quickly move to another.

Normally calves are first suckled effectively within a few hours of birth. Cows with pendulous udders, however, and those whose under-lines rise towards the fore-end, instead of the hind-end, often have their calves' teat-seeking efforts deployed in the wrong direction. In such cases first sucklings may be seriously delayed.

*Pigs.* The sow's normal suckling position is one of full extension on one of its sides. Normally sows lie as much on one side as the other, but some sows prefer lying consistently on one particular side. This often results in a reduction of milk-flow, since the ventral row of teats may not be so satisfactorily attended and massaged. Other sows prefer to stand during suckling (Fig. 42); this may also hinder the piglets' massaging activities which stimulate milk let-down and once again may result in reduced milk-yield.

At an early stage, a social order is established with regard to sucking activities: the teats in the pectoral and inguinal regions are first occupied (Fig. 43). The teat order may be observed in that piglets often suck from the corresponding teats when their dam turns on to her other side. But variations may occur when there are a different number of teats on each side, or if there is some confusion in the middle region. The heavier piglets tend to occupy the softer pectoral region and evidence suggests that the position of the piglets with regard to their usual teats is influenced to some extent by the odour of their neighbours. Thus when a sow's udder is coated with mud or a foreign odour the piglets are still able to locate the teats they normally suck and do so without too much difficulty. Sometimes a piglet will try to move away from the teats in the inguinal region towards the middle and this may cause momentary confusion, but otherwise the teat order is well adhered to by the litter.

Occasionally piglets become quiescent while still grasping the teats and massaging has been discontinued. They will sometimes sleep through to the next feeding time. This has the advantage of preserving the order of the littler whilst feeding and helps to discourage aggressive behaviour between the neonates at that time. Aggressive interactions in the litter often precipitate deaths through inanition. A piglet which is forced out of its suckling position becomes disorientated and may wander. This may result in the sow crushing the stray when she shifts her position or attempts to rise to her feet. Similarly, displacement occurs in large litters (particularly those over fourteen in number) when one or more piglets are unable to find a permanent position in the teat order.

There are three definite stages in the process of nursing under-taken by the sow and her young: nosing, lactation and massaging. When nursing commences all the members of the litter are involved in nosing the udder. Occasionally one piglet will shift to the sow's

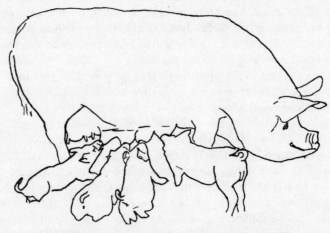

Fig. 42.   Sow suckling in the less common standing position. The piglets
sink to recumbency as the let-down progresses and they become
satiated. The largest piglet (on the anterior teat as is often the
case) shows recumbency and repletion last. (tracing)

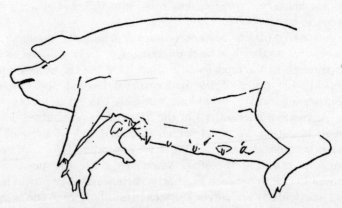

Fig. 43.   Selection of the preferred upper, anterior teat by lone piglet; a
basic mechanism in the teat order phenomenon in litter organization. (tracing)

Fig. 44.   Sow nosing a 'litter-rep' in pre-letdown. (tracing)

head while the remainder continue to nose and massage (Fig. 44). The nosing activities last for about 1 minute before milk let-down commences. Each piglet pushes its snout forcefully upwards and into the udder. This promotes an easing of tension in the udder and stimulates the let-down of milk. The period during which milk release occurs and the piglets are suckled is relatively short: about 13 to 14 seconds, during which time the piglets suck intensely (Fig. 45). When milk flow has ceased, the neonates engage in a

Fig. 45.   A litter of piglets sucking vigorously during the sow's let-down of milk. Note the contraction of tail muscles characterizing this event. (tracing)

Fig. 46. Piglets drawing sow's teats at the termination of the let-down phase. (tracing)

further massaging period which lasts for a varying length of time (Fig. 46).

*Sheep* (see also pp. 68–69). Lambs suck more frequently in the first few weeks following parturition than the young of any other domestic farm animal. This high frequency of sucking lasts for no more than a few weeks. Whether there is any physiological basis for this behaviour, however, is doubtful. Lambs sucking at hourly intervals gain no more weight than those sucking at 2-hourly intervals. Lambs often suck when they are frightened or subjected to stresses.

Fig. 47. Ewe suckling newborn lamb. The ewe's attention has been drawn by the lamb's vigorous tail wagging which completes the circle of nursing stimulation. (tracing)

Initially, in the early post-parturient period, ewes allow their young to suck at will. They also allow one twin lamb to suck while the other is absent, but 4 to 6 weeks postpartum ewes allow sucking to take place less frequently and permit twin neonates to suck only when both show a desire to do so. By this time suckling is reduced to about 10 to 20 seconds on each occasion.

# IMPRINTING

The special behavioural affiliation between the neonate and its mother has been termed 'imprinting'. The term alludes to the significant and lasting impression made on the young animal's behaviour by its neonatal environment, including the dam's identifying characteristics. The process of imprinting takes place in a comparatively short period of time sometimes referred to as the 'critical period'.

In sheep the critical period normally takes place a few hours following parturition and involves the neonate's environment as well as the form of the mother. It has been said that if the surrounding area makes no significant impression on it, the neonate may fail to adopt fully a territory which it regards as home. The establishment of imprinting is thought to be less a purely visual mechanism, than an olfactory one where the young animal is able

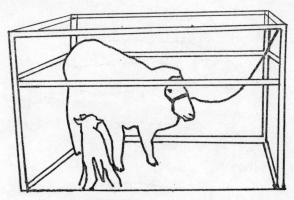

Fig. 48.   With the critical period in the puerperal ewe passed, attempts at fostering an alien lamb require a lengthy association between the lamb and the ewe in restraint. (drawing)

to absorb, amongst other factors, smells and tastes that may influence its feeding behaviour even later on in life.

Today less emphasis is placed on the briefness and irrevocability of imprinting, and there are indications that the subliminal nature of imprinting is not quite as dramatic as was at first reported. Studies have shown that if a newborn lamb is taken from the ewe an hour or so after birth and returned after 8 hours, the young lamb will still be accepted by the mother. It is important that the dam involved is in the critical period and that by licking and grooming of the neonate its specific odour becomes identifiable to her, thereby establishing the attachment. However it has been found that if the neonate lamb is removed immediately after birth and returned to the ewe within a period of 2 to 4 hours, it is likely to be totally rejected. It is essential, therefore, that the dam fully identifies the odour of her young before and during the critical period.

## SOCIAL INTERACTIONS

*Pigs.* Almost immediately after they are born, piglets begin to develop cohesive interactions towards each other. This ensures the maximum likelihood of survival and the optimum development

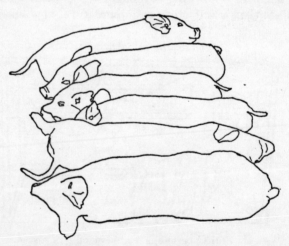

Fig. 49. Typical huddling in a litter of piglets. The overall geometry of the arrangement is notable. (tracing)

of the litter as a whole. As has previously been stated, the precocious nature of very young piglets allows them to walk, suck and begin to establish a social order within minutes of birth. However, in establishing this order, young piglets will bite and slash each other frequently during the first few days postpartum. This agonistic behaviour is implemented by sharp canine deciduous teeth.

Piglets are more susceptible to changes in the surrounding temperature than other domestic neonates and prefer an ambient temperature in the region of 28°C. The sensitivity of their skin and lack of body hair precipitates huddling behaviour (Fig. 49) in cold weather. In order to preserve body heat, the piglets lie close together and parallel to one another but facing in opposite directions. Those in the centre of the huddle, however, usually face the same way and when cold is extreme the litter huddles in such a way as to form a very closely knit group. Some of the piglets climb on to the backs of others forming an upper row where they lay themselves between the divisions of the piglets below.

*Cattle.* Social interactions begin to develop in calves when they start to play with others of the same age and to form 'nursery groups'. Within these groups calves may simply rest or graze together and are watched over by an attendant cow. Grooming activities also take place amongst the young at this time. After weaning a young animal joins the herd, adopting a position in the social order, and in doing so irrevocably breaks the relationship with its mother. Within the herd calf groups are formed with a hierarchy of their own and the young animal begins its development to adulthood. Initially, when they join a mixed group, young bulls are dominated by the females, but after 18 months or so during which time fighting may take place, they come to dominate all the females.

*Sheep.* The development of social interactions in lambs is less obvious. The strong leader–followership aspect of behaviour in sheep is seen when lambs follow the older ewes or their own mothers. In all-male flocks the young rams follow the oldest members of the group, but gradually they develop some form of independence and it becomes easier to separate the animal from the main flock if required. The dominance order in sheep develops relatively slowly.

*Horses.* Young stallions which have only recently joined the troop often form bachelor groupings during the early mating seasons. They usually cooperate with older males which move them together, keeping them at a distance from the mares and fillies. As they get older, however, the bachelor foals become less tolerant

Fig. 50. Brood mare grazing with foal in close lateral bond association. (tracing)

of this activity and fighting sometimes occurs (often with the result that the younger stallion defeats his opponent). Young foals show little sense of a social hierarchy and may walk into foreign territories and consequently disturb other animals. Thus, a mare tends to suppress any wandering tendencies by her foal at least until it is able to run to safety.

# SUPPLEMENTARY READING

ALEXANDER, G. & WILLIAMS, D. (1966) Teat-seeking activity in lambs during the first hours of life. *Anim. Behav., 14*, 166–176.

CROSS, B. A. (1961) Neural control of lactation. In: *Milk: the Mammary Gland and its Secretion*, ed. S. K. Kon & A. T. Cowie, vol. 1, pp. 229–277. New York: Academic Press.

EWBANK, R. (1964) Observations on the suckling habits of twin lambs. *Anim. Behav., 12*, 34–37.

EWBANK, R. (1967) Nursing and suckling behaviour amongst Clun Forest ewes and lambs. *Anim. Behav., 15*, 251–258.

EWBANK, R. & MASON, A. C. (1967) A note on the sucking behaviour of twin lambs reared as singles. *Anim. Prod., 2*, 417–420.

GILL, J. C. & THOMSON, W. (1956) Observations on the behaviour of suckling pigs. *Br. J. Anim. Behav., 4*, 46–51.

HERSHER, L., RICHMOND, J. B. & MOORE, A. U. (1963) Maternal behavior in sheep and goats. In: *Maternal Behavior in Mammals*, ed. H. L. Rheingold, pp. 203–232. New York: Wiley.

HESS, E. H. (1962) Imprinting and the 'critical period' concept. In: *Roots of Behavior*, ed. E. L. Bliss, pp. 254–263. New York: Harper Bros.

KLOPFER, P. H., ADAMS, D. K. & KLOPFER, M. S. (1964) Maternal 'imprinting' in goats. *Proc. natn. Acad. Sci. U.S.A., 52*, 911–914.

McBRIDE, G. (1963) The 'teat order' and communication in young pigs. *Anim. Behav., 11*, 53–56.

MUNRO, J. (1956) Observations on the suckling behaviour of young lambs. *Br. J. Anim. Behav., 4*, 34–36.

SELMAN, I. E., McEWAN, A. D. & FISHER, E. W. (1970) Studies on natural suckling in cattle during the first eight hours post-partum. *Anim. Behav., 18*, 276–283.

SMITH, F. V., VAN-TOLLER, C. & BOYES, T. (1966) The 'critical period' in the attachment of lambs and ewes. *Anim. Behav., 14*, 120–125.

# Part IV
# ABNORMAL BEHAVIOUR

# 14.

# Behaviour and Clinical Disorders

BEHAVIOUR relating to manifestations of ill health can be called clinical behaviour. Literally, the expression indicates behaviour noted during visual examination of the sick animal, and therefore relates to behavioural manifestations of illness. In fact, altered behaviour is the first indication of illness and thus animal behaviour and veterinary diagnosis have long been associated closely. There are numerous references to the behaviour of sick animals in the classical literature of Ancient Greece and today it can be said that all practising veterinarians rely heavily on behavioural observations in aiding arrival at a correct diagnosis of ill health.

There are many common diseases in animals in which the diagnosis is based primarily on behavioural evidence. Examples include: deficiency diseases such as aphosphorosis, metabolic diseases such as hypomagnesaemia and hypocalcaemia, and infectious conditions such as botulism and rabies. As a result every veterinary clinician is, to some extent, a practical animal behaviourist. This fact has been recognized openly now in all major veterinary training colleges by the introduction of courses in veterinary ethology or animal behaviour.

The link between altered behaviour and the diseased state is so close that there is a tendency for obviously abnormal behaviour (which presumably occurs in response to an abnormal physical state), to be used as the identification index for particular diseases. For this reason a number of diseases are known by behavioural descriptions. Examples of these include staggers, nymphomania, star-gazing, gid (giddiness), lockjaw and other more vague clinical syndromes such as 'the wanderer foal' and 'the fading piglet' syndromes.

# CLINICAL VETERINARY ETHOLOGY

A scientific interest in the altered behaviour arising from changes in health, i.e. the objective study of behaviour in diseased animals, is termed clinical veterinary ethology. We are, at present, at a very early stage in the study of this subject as an entity. There is a good deal of knowledge of a practical nature relating to this subject, and it is desirable now to organize the more academic aspects of this branch of ethology.

In Chapter 2 it is shown how attempts are often made to relate behavioural patterns to physiological mechanisms by means of concepts; the concepts of drive, of stimulation and of motivation are considered. We have already seen how an ethological study must recognize the effects of forms of stimulation and the ways in which stimulation operates. External stimulation and the reactions of the animal body together develop the essential mechanism behind each behavioural pattern. This view of the basis of behaviour holds equally well both for the normal and the abnormal functions of the animal body as a whole.

Since it is possible, in many circumstances, to relate behaviour to physiological mechanisms, it should also be possible to relate behaviour to pathological conditions. Furthermore, specific behaviour patterns may be associated with pathological processes which do not reside in the nervous system, although it must be recognized that many general diseases, by extension, ultimately involve the nervous system.

As the study of animal behaviour becomes more precise, more demanding and more sophisticated, it becomes clearer that the relationship between behaviour and physiological processes must be emphasized. Likewise, veterinary work dealing with animals that have some organic malfunction must attempt to recognize and relate abnormal behaviour patterns with pathological conditions of the animal body and to do so in a systematic fashion. This has not been done in the past since its necessity was not appreciated. If it is important to be systematic about the connection between normal behaviour and normal bodily function it is no less important to relate abnormal behaviour with bodily malfunction. One of the simplest systematic approaches is the anatomical one, in which an attempt is made to relate observed behaviour to a pathological condition of anatomical body systems such as skeletal, muscular, locomotor and digestive systems. This is probably the method adopted by the majority of veterinary surgeons. One obvious difficulty in this approach, however, is that pathological processes probably all involve more than one body system; this causes major difficulties in correlating specific behaviour and signs of disease with symptoms of a specific disease.

In spite of the importance attached to abnormal behaviour in clinical veterinary knowledge, the descriptions of abnormal behaviour in veterinary literature are generally couched in subjective terms. Such descriptions give little indication of how abnormalities in behaviour differ quantitatively from normal behaviour. Veterinary literature dealing with clinical conditions is peppered with such expressions as 'stupid posture', 'painful expression', 'dullness', etc. These terms do nothing to convey meaning to uninitiated readers. Moreover they do very little to enhance the scientific nature of clinical veterinary literature. For the future, one of the foremost aims of the clinical veterinary ethologist must be the accurate measurement and description of the temporal and spatial organization of abnormal behaviour in his patients. By this means, clinical veterinary ethology could develop a more penetrating clinical acumen, and lead to a deeper understanding of animals in a diseased state and more efficient information transfer in teaching situations.

One must hasten to acknowledge the fact that the present state of knowledge of the behaviour of animals is largely satisfactory at the practical level. The veterinarian working under practical and field conditions inevitably becomes aware of many aspects of farm animal behaviour. But this type of practitioner increasingly needs and uses behavioural knowledge and requires the expertise necessary for the accurate assessment of the situation. This knowledge in the main relates to the handling of animals, their breeding activities, the behavioural signs of illness and also to their habits, all of which can lead to hazardous situations in the spread of diseases.

# BEHAVIOUR AS A DIAGNOSTIC AID

While the behaviour of a normal and healthy farm animal is clearly the concern of many people, it is primarily the veterinarian who is required to understand abnormal behavioural activity. Increasingly the veterinary profession has its attention directed towards conditions of distress, discomfort, probable pain and deprivation in the farm animals. These conditions are stressors, and stress is a disease the manifestations of which are many. Appreciation of this fact makes the veterinarian better able to guide animal users and producers in the optimum and acceptable conditions of maintenance for farm animals in modern husbandry. This newer role for the veterinarian depends largely on the development of veterinary ethology and the use of abnormal behaviour as an aid to diagnosis. At the present stage in the development of veterinary ethology it is impossible to deal with this topic comprehensively. All that can be done is to consider a number of clinical circumstances where diagnosis can be established on the basis of an animal's behaviour. Even this assumes a full and accurate knowledge of the normal behaviour of that type of farm animal on the part of the observer.

## *Posture*

The postural behaviour of animals is one of the commonest behavioural features to undergo change in diseased conditions. It is therefore essential to appreciate normal posture as a basis for recognizing postural abnormalities for clinical purposes. The following are the main circumstances under which animals adopt abnormal postures:

1. Mechanical conditions involving loss of support or stability by the animal
2. Nervous conditions in which there is a reduction in adequate neural function to maintain muscular tone
3. Painful conditions which make it possible for the animal to maintain customary posture
4. Permanent adaptive changes which the animal may have acquired as a result of prior experience of any of the circumstances mentioned above

*Mechanical conditions* influencing postural behaviour are many and the following few examples are given as illustrations. Fracture of the metacarpus in the horse makes it impossible for the animal to take any weight at all on the affected leg. Fracture of the humerus also leads to lack of mechanical support and a grossly altered posture. Severance of the flexor tendons in the horse leads to a sinking of the fetlock and a turning up of the toe. Spastic paresis of the leg in cattle results in a contraction of the gastrocnemius muscle as a result of which the affected limb becomes shorter. Congenitally contracted tendons in foals also make normal posture impossible.

*Nervous conditions* which can create abnormal postures include radial paralysis in the horse following prolonged recumbency during anaesthesia, for example. A lesion in the cervical vertebrae causes the condition of wobbler in the horse the main characteristic of which is a stiff neck. Abscessation of the lumbar vertebrae can cause it to adopt the 'dog-sitting' position for lengthy periods.

*Painful conditions* which cause abnormal postural behaviour include suppurative arthritis and osteomyelitis of fetlocks. The latter condition causes a tucking-under of the hind legs. Gonitis (inflammation of the stifle joint) occurs in horses, principally, causing them to point the ground with the toe of the affected hind limb.

*Permanent adaptive changes* may arise in a condition such as laminitis which can occur in all the hooved animals; those which have experienced laminitis for some period of time sometimes learn to walk on 'tip-toe' with the forelegs. This position appears to minimize pain. The adoption of this posture also means that the hind legs of the animal are brought further forward beneath it. Spinal abscessation in the pig may be the result of tail-biting and this may cause the posture of a hind leg to be altered. The common condition of foot-rot in sheep can lead, in some cases, to a state of osteomyelitis. In this condition, the affected animal frequently adopts a kneeling posture. Cattle which are kept in stalls and have experienced a form of chronic laminitis sometimes learn to stand back in the stall so that their heels overhang the standing. This posture allows the animal's weight to be transferred to its toes thereby reducing pain. Cattle which have suffered acute pain in both medial digits may stand with forelegs crossed to take all the weight on the lateral digits. This condition sometimes occurs in abscessation of the sole and fracture of the third phalanx of one leg. In cattle it is sometimes noted that the limbs are advanced and rotated outwards taking the weight off the lateral digits. This condition is referred to as 'wing shoulder'. The condition is found in various states and sometimes appears to be due to laminitis and at other times is related to aphosphorosis. Cattle, with wing shoulder, when made to walk do so apparently normally.

Other behavioural postures include a tripod form of stance when one leg is shortened, for example, in spastic paresis. Cattle, which have experienced pain in their feet for some period of time, sometimes lie with their hind legs extended out behind them. This appears to relieve pain in the feet.

In a study of posture as an aid to diagnosis it must be remembered that many postural abnormalities are not shown unless the animal is at rest in its usual environment. For this reason, patient and quiet observation of the animal may be necessary before abnormalities of posture can be detected and appreciated.

## Reflexes

Reflexes should not be studied as isolated phenomena but as actions of the whole animal. Part II of this book dealt with some normal animal reflexes; mutual grooming and stretching after rising are probably the two most common simple reflexes seen in healthy stock. Several factors, including illness in general, can inhibit grooming and stretching reflexes. In cattle another reflex 'tongueing of the nostrils' may be inhibited during illness. It has also been suggested that the eructation reflex in ruminants becomes inhibited in many illnesses and, as a consequence of this, distension of the rumen develops and becomes painful. This further inhibits eructating reflexes and leads to the condition of bloat which is seen associated with various illnesses in ruminants. Recognition of these minor reflexes in the normal behaviour of cattle is an indication of sound health and, consequently, their absence suggests that health is impaired.

## Pain

The farm animals manifest pain in various ways. These ways depend upon the site and the severity of the pain and also on the temperament of the individual animal. The observation of pain and the identification of its source obviously plays a very important part in clinical diagnosis.

Collectively the signs of pain in animals give an impression of uneasiness, but the behaviour of an animal in pain has certain specific features which are recognizable. The facial expression of an animal in pain is often quite characteristic; usually there is a fixed stare within the eye. The eye is not as mobile within its orbit as in the healthy animal. The eyelids tend to be slightly puckered. The ears of animals in pain, notably horses, are usually held slightly back and fixed in that position for long periods. Animals suffering pain usually have dilated nostrils. These facial signs collectively give an animal a 'worried' expression (to use a subjective term). In pain the animal is often seen to turn its head to one side or the other, looking at one or other flank.

In colic or abdominal pain, the animal (and the horse in particular) shows various abnormalities of posture. Animals with persistent colic may show unusual recumbent behaviour; at other times they may adopt an unusual stance. Horses may back into a corner of a loose box, and both horses and cattle can sometimes be observed standing pushing their heads against a wall (Fig. 51) when a painful condition is present in the abdomen. Abdominal pain may cause the animal to lie down frequently, rising repeatedly

Fig. 51. A bullock pushing its head against a wall. (tracing)

after short intervals. In between these periods of recumbency, a horse with colic may scrape at its bedding with a forefoot, whilst slowly pivoting around on its hind legs.

In conditions of severe pain, animals often show a full extension of the nostrils, rolling the eyes in the head, extending the head and neck vigorously and groaning. Some horses lie on their backs in a position of dorsal recumbency with all four legs held in the air. This abnormal posture may be maintained for up to 15 minutes. More violent manifestations of pain are shown by horses on some occasions: the animal may throw itself down, may roll from side to side, may rise and walk into objects in its surroundings. In this state the horse seems oblivious to its surroundings and all of its behaviour is indicative of severe pain.

Painful conditions of the skeleton frequently result in changes of posture in ways that have already been described above.

## BEHAVIOUR IN SPECIFIC DISEASES

Lameness in cattle can be caused by a great variety of circumstances but one particular type of condition, namely, *abscessation of the solar matrix* results in the affected limb being cast inwards or outwards, depending on which digit is affected. The lameness pattern in this condition is quite different to that seen in laminitis.

*Tetanus* produces a distinctive behaviour with rigid stance and stilted gait as its principal feature.

*Cerebral cortical necrosis* affects behaviour significantly, causing incoordination and patterns of recumbency, which are quite characteristic.

In *muscular dystrophy*, affected calves walk in a characteristic style with the scapulae rising as much as 10 centimetres above the vertebral column giving a 'broken front spring' appearance.

Cattle with *hypocalcaemia* adopt a very characteristic recumbent posture and many of them show an equally characteristic 'S' bend of the neck whilst recumbent.

In *hypomagnesaemia*, it is common to observe greatly increased excitability in the behaviour of the affected animal. This excitability is evident in such behavioural features as unusual and excessive flicking of the eyes and ears and in an unusual style of walking.

*Urolithiasis* occurs quite commonly in rams which are housed and heavily fed. The condition is associated with characteristic behaviour including grating of the teeth, straining and arching of the back.

In *gangreneous mastitis*, affected ewes characteristically draw one hind leg behind the other while walking. An animal's general posture indicates a toxic state and the head is often held low.

In other animals, conditions such as *ear infections* and *mouth ulcerations* create characteristic behavioural signs.

Since this chapter is concerned with illustrating the connection between farm animal behaviour and disease, two examples have been chosen which detail this relationship. These examples are among the most common clinical conditions which are dealt with in the routine of veterinary field work, namely cystic ovarian disease and milk fever in cattle.

## Cystic Ovarian Disease in Cattle

This is characterized by the presence of enlarged and cystic follicles on the ovary. The behavioural correlates in this condition are well known. Natural oestrogen levels in the blood are raised and oestrous behaviour is affected. Oestrous periodicity seems normal in approximately 33% of cases, but alongside this there may be a continuous, low degree of clinical oestrus as a background to the pattern of overt oestrous periodicity. In these cases there is a lower level of oestrous periodicity to be seen in the animals most of the time with peaks of oestrous behaviour coinciding with the normal cyclical pattern of oestrous activity.

In about 80% of clinical cases restless behaviour is very conspicuous. This appears to be related to the fact that the rate of thyroxine secretion in cattle with cystic ovarian disease is about double that in normal animals. The remaining 20% of clinical cases show different behavioural abnormalities. One facet of this disease is the virile cow syndrome (adrenal virilism). The first change is usually a deepening of the voice and an increase in vocal activity so that the animals are heard roaring in masculine fashion. These cows also start to show 'digging' behaviour with their horns and eventually will persistently ride other cattle. Aggression in these animals is markedly increased. In another group, possibly the largest one, there is a typical feminizing behaviour with increased production of vaginal mucus and frequent acceptance of mounting by other cattle. Increased pawing activity may be seen in some of these animals. Among the various forms of masculine behaviour, digging with the forefeet is most consistently observed.

## Milk Fever in Cattle

Milk fever is a complex disturbance of the mineral concentrations and ratios in the blood of cows. The typical case occurs postpartum and within 96 hours of parturition. The behaviour observed during this condition is caused by a biochemical disturbance in the plasma minerals and the physiological processes ensuing from this upset. The physiological behaviour pattern is not fully understood. This alteration of the mineral levels in blood can however explain the overall picture in a cow with milk fever. Calcium is essential for normal neuromuscular excitability, normal muscle contraction and normal transmission of nerve impulses. When the plasma-calcium level is decreased all three of these activities are increased to an abnormally high level. Thus the behaviour of the animal takes the form of increased nervous excitability, incoordination of movements, paresis and eventually coma. To a certain extent general behaviour can thus be explained; but the clinician can distinguish three main behavioural stages in milk fever. These are detailed below.

*Early Stages.* In the early stages of the disturbance the general behaviour is that of discomfort and anxiety. The cow is disinclined to move, has a depressed facial expression with staring eyes in which the pupils are dilated, grinds her teeth and often makes intermittent paddling movements with her hind legs. She is apparently experiencing anxiety due to the progressing metabolic upset. There is complete bowel stasis, normally with a full rectum. Often the cow produces exaggerated abdominal efforts to defaecate (to little or no avail) and she quite often has a full bladder.

*Excitable Stage and Paresis.* As the condition progresses, the pattern of behaviour can vary further.

1. The cow, in her natural surroundings at pasture, may start to show some increased excitement, by sweating and becoming more alert under the effect of the decreasing plasma-calcium level. She may even show some degree of incoordination in her movements. In general as her powers of balance recede she is inclined to wander stiff-legged, swaying a little, to a quiet corner of the field and then subside to a position of sternal recumbency.

2. The cow in the byre often shows a more excitable behaviour pattern during the disturbance. She appears to be hypersensitive to noise, her ears are alert and continually on the move like a 'radar vane'. Unless the conditions in the byre are very quiet she is disinclined to lie down as her sense of balance recedes. She adopts a variety of postures in attempting to retain her balance. If her feet should slip she will show exaggerated posturing of the legs and body to regain balance. She tends to remain standing as long as possible and can be seen trembling and stiff-legged until she collapses in the stall.

The more thoughtful and understanding owner or cowman removes the cow, in which he anticipates the disturbance, to quieter and safer premises—a box or a yard. Once there the behaviour of the cow tends to resemble that of a cow at pasture. She may still show typical posturing for a period of time (especially if she has very recently been moved to the box) but will usually lie down before her sense of balance becomes too impaired. If approached while standing she often tends to be aggressive. She may attempt to kick out, even although she may almost collapse in the effort, or may lower her head to butt the intruder.

*Coma.* Once the cow is recumbent, she becomes more placid, although sometimes showing hyper-excitability and sweating if approached. If she is disturbed at this stage, she shows excessive excitability and may eventually roll into lateral recumbency with legs extended in spasms. As coma supervenes, she either remains in sternal recumbency and lowers her head and neck to the ground, or rolls over into lateral recumbency.

The variety of behavioural patterns, as seen by the clinician, appears to revolve round the degree of excitability engendered in the cow. The degree of excitability appears to be influenced by the surroundings and management of the cow, although one can attempt to explain it to a certain extent by quoting differing blood mineral levels.

The behaviour pattern developed in milk fever can be explained physiologically, but clinically once the disturbance is set in motion the behaviour pattern appears to be governed partly by the surroundings, partly by the management of the animal and partly by a degree of fear engendered by these factors and by the presence of man.

# SUPPLEMENTARY READING

Fox, M. W. (1968) *Abnormal Behavior in Animals*. London: Saunders.

Fraser, A. F. (1963) The significance of the 'pushing' syndrome. *Anim. Behav.*, *11*, 51–52.

Littlejohn, A. (1969). An approach to clinical veterinary ethology. *Br. vet. J.*, *125*, 46–48.

Littlejohn, A. (1970) The behaviour of horses recovering from anaesthesia. *Br. vet. J.*, *126*, 617–621.

Rossdale, P. D. (1967) Clinical studies on the newborn thoroughbred foal. *Br. vet. J.*, *123*, 470–481.

# 15.

# Anomalous Behaviour

VETERINARY workers are by no means unfamiliar with abnormal behaviour in animals. Ill health in animals may first be detected as a result of a change in their behaviour. It is often found that alterations in the normal behaviour patterns are due to organic conditions in the animals. Indeed reduced activity, unusual behavioural features and unsound body movement are usually due to such conditions as infections, deranged metabolism or some gross structural defect.

There are a number of forms of unusual or anomalous behaviour which are found to be unrelated to any specific or recognizable organic cause. These have sometimes been referred to as primary behavioural disorders. This group, which is referred to here as behavioural anomalies, has really only been studied to a limited extent, mostly during the last decade. Some forms of abnormal behaviour are of importance on economic grounds, but all of them are important on clinical grounds. Even where anomalous behaviour cannot be related to some physical defect in the animal, it clearly indicates that the subject is not in harmony with its environment and that its function as a unit must therefore be considered to be impaired.

Today animal scientists are beginning to realize that many forms of abnormal behaviour are related to noxious stimuli or stressors in an animal's environment. Stress is a dynamic state with significant behavioural manifestations among which displacement activities feature very prominently. There is every prospect that more detailed study of anomalous behaviour in farm animals in the near future could improve the diagnosis of stress, which like so many other diseases, undoubtedly occurs with differing degrees of intensity and variations in the signs displayed. Already it has been learned that when the 'quantity' and 'quality' of an animal's environment are reduced there is an increased probability of abnormal behaviour developing. The decline in environmental quality includes a reduction in the variability of the animal's surroundings. Inferior environments of this type are closely linked with anomalous behaviour such as cannibalism, reduction in appetite, stereotyped movements, poor parental care, over-aggressiveness, unresponsiveness, tail-biting, cribbing (Fig. 52), etc. Many of those behavioural features which have for many years been regarded as vices are in fact forms of anomalous behaviour resulting from exposure to environmental inadequacies.

Fig. 52.   Crib-biting. (tracing)

The incidence of anomalous behaviour in animal husbandry appears to be on the increase. With modern animal production methods it is sometimes considered adequate to provide the animal with facilities for nutrition, rest and reproduction but little else. The environmental facilities afforded to pigs, for example, are commonly very limited; yet field studies on pig behaviour have built up an ethogram for this animal along the lines already described in Chapter 7. Thus the free ranging pig is commonly found to spend 40% of its time at rest, 35% of its time exploring and investigating features of its environment, 15% of its time feeding and drinking and 10% on sundry other activities. The modern intensive husbandry methods do not normally allow pigs

to indulge in voluntary activities to this extent, and the inadequacies of environmental conditions are eventually revealed in
overt anomalous behaviour by the animals.

However tedious it may be it is essential to lay down some
definition that will divide normal behaviour from abnormal or
anomalous behaviour so that the latter can be pinpointed more
certainly. In general, if observations establish constancy in a
specific feature of behaviour in the majority of animals under
similar conditions, it can be taken that the behaviour observed is
normal for that situation. However, more precise guides to classi-
fication of behaviour are required. Undoubtedly of prime importance is a decision as to whether observed behavioural features are
appropriate both in their biological purpose and their degree of
manifestation; inappropriate behaviour can be termed anomalous.
Again, as has been stressed several times in the text already, if a
sound decision on the normality or abnormality of behaviour is to
be reached it is essential for the observer to know intimately the
full range of normal behaviour in a given species. Decisions regarding the normality of behaviour are necessarily limited to those
responses occurring in recognizable situations associated with
identifiable stimuli. With these guidelines a number of examples
of anomalous behaviour in animals do become recognizable.

# ANOMALOUS INGESTIVE BEHAVIOUR

Anomalous ingestive behaviour is essentially related to aberrations
in taste, i.e. in the choice of foods. A great many examples of
aberrant feeding have been noted in farm animals; these include:
sand-eating in horses; licking and ingestion of foreign bodies in
cattle; pulling, tearing and swallowing of each others' fleece in
sheep; cannibalism in pigs and coprophagia. Practically every farm
animal species provides occasional cases in which individuals show
a marked preferential consumption of food of poor quality such as
soiled litter, faeces, earth, wood and cloth. Pica (or depraved
appetite) is by no means an uncommon symptom of certain
deficiency diseases such as aphosphorosis. Nevertheless, these other
forms of aberrant ingestive behaviour are not always identifiable
as being part of a syndrome of a deficiency disease. In addition to

aberrations of taste, anomalies in quantitative ingestive behaviour are known. Anorexia—a significant reduction in appetite—can occur occasionally without any organic disease being recognizable.

## ANOMALOUS MALE SEXUAL BEHAVIOUR

Sex drive in male farm animals is commonly referred to as libido. Excessive libido is seldom considered to be a behavioural abnormality in animals, but an abnormal reduction in the level of sex drive in male stud animals is by no means uncommon. Indeed it has been suggested that *reduced sex drive* constitutes one of the principal causes of infertility in male animals. Some forms of impotence in farm animals are undoubtedly related to physical defects such as arthritis or other orthopaedic conditions which affect the mobility of the animal; but in a great many instances impotence is not evidently related to a physical impairment. It is suggested that in many of these cases the specific defective behaviour is genetically determined since this form of impotence is not infrequently encountered in certain breeds.

Male sex drive certainly has a heritable nature; this has been shown in bulls. The low sex drive of impotent bulls results in these animals having abnormally long reaction times when required to mate with cows under controlled conditions. While 50% of bulls make a positive attempt at mating within 2 minutes of being presented to an oestrous cow, the broad population of bulls has an average reaction time of approximately 12 minutes. Bulls with reaction times of 30 minutes or as much as 1 hour are clearly, to some degree, impotent. During these protracted reaction times impotent animals characteristically show none of the sundry features of sexual interest normally shown by bulls. Attention is not directed towards the female, for much of the time, and the behavioural indications of sexual arousal, such as pumping actions of the tail-head and nosing and licking of the perineal regions of the cow, are not shown.

One particular type of impotence in bulls has been termed *psychic impotence*; this has been described by many workers in the field of animal reproduction. An affected bull usually shows a strong sex drive and mounts readily. When mounted however, although appearing to engage in normal movements, he fails to cover the cow satisfactorily. His hind feet are not brought close to the hind feet of the cow and close genital apposition does not occur between the two. After some futile pelvic thrusting by the bull, the mating attempt ceases. Such episodes may be repeated many times without effect. These bulls have been found to be capable of ejaculating satisfactorily into an artificial vagina, and can be used as semen donors. In addition their sexual behaviour often seems to return to normal after a protracted period of sexual rest. Psychic impotence has been observed in bulls of various breeds and age groups. No physical cause has yet been ascertained for this type of impotence.

Anomalous sexual behaviour can quite commonly be observed in immature male animals. *Inexperience of mating* can be responsible for apparently abnormal behaviour which commonly takes the form of lateral mounting (Fig. 53). This is shown by young

Fig. 53.   Lateral mounting by a maiden bull. (drawing)

bulls, in particular, when they repeatedly make mounting attempts over the sides of cows and may exhaust themselves before any effective mating can be performed. Some bulls, it seems, require time to learn the chain of behavioural actions necessary for effective mating. It may well be that in many of these animals puberty occurs much later than is commonly supposed. Lateral mounting certainly seems to be more of a problem in animals that are put to stud very soon after they have attained the chronological age by which puberty is expected to have occurred.

Abnormal sexual behaviour termed *somnolent* is not infrequently found to be a cause of impotence, particularly in aged bulls. In this condition, an animal shows protracted reaction times during which he lays his chin on the hindquarters of the cow and stands still with eyes closed, making no positive mounting attempts. Fatigue of the sex drive has obviously occurred in these animals.

# ANOMALOUS FEMALE SEXUAL BEHAVIOUR

The transient behavioural state of oestrus during which the female animal consorts with the male and participates in mating activities is also subject to anomalous features. These range from subnormal oestrous behaviour to abnormally increased manifestations of oestrus.

In a significant percentage of animals the physiological state of oestrus appears to occur without the normally associated behavioural features being manifested. This condition is referred to as *suboestrus* or *silent heat* and is something of a major problem in farm animal breeding. It occurs, for example, in mares and is also quite common in cows in heavy lactation. Studies of this condition in cattle have reported an incidence ranging from 18 to 30% among animals that were physically normal. In one study it was noted that there was a significantly higher incidence of suboestrus in animals that were low down in the social hierarchy of the herd. It has been suggested that sexual functions are as likely to be suppressed in conditions of stress in the female animal as in the male.

Even when oestrous behaviour is revealed the level of manifestation is by no means constant. The opinion has long been expressed that certain breeds of cattle, for example, have a hereditary predisposition for weak behavioural signs of heat or oestrus. Various researchers have noted, however, that the apparent intensity of the behavioural signs of oestrus in cattle is seldom consistent from one oestrous period to another even in the same animal, and it is now generally recognized that the repeatability of behaviour at successive oestruses is low. In the mare, however, the display of oestrous behaviour appears to be fairly constant for a given animal. In this animal also, limited displays of oestrus are quite common. *Continuous* or *excessively frequent oestrus* is a well-known disorder among dairy cattle. Today it is recognized that this condition invariably relates to cystic ovarian degeneration and for this reason it has been described in the preceding chapter.

## ANOMALOUS MATERNAL BEHAVIOUR

Epimeletic behaviour is the care-giving behaviour of the dam towards her offspring and the several aspects of epimelesis are subject to dysfunction. The main forms of anomalous maternal behaviour in farm animals involve repulsion of the newborn animal by the mother.

In pigs cannibalism is the most dramatic manifestation of this type of anomalous behaviour but other less spectacular forms of abnormal maternal behaviour occur. These include failure to groom the newborn animal, refusal to suckle (Fig. 54) and aggressive displays directed towards the neonate.

Various forms of anomalous maternal behaviour have been distinguished in sheep. Collectively these forms of anomalous

Fig. 54.   Sow with a young litter covering mammary region in abnormal uncooperative maternal behaviour. (tracing)

Fig. 55.   A pregnant ewe stealing the first twin while the second is being delivered. (tracing)

behaviour contribute considerably to lamb mortalities. Examples include:

1. Premature onset of maternal behaviour. Aged ewes, in particular, are liable to show an abnormal interest in newborn lambs before the birth of their own (Fig. 55). This can occur as early as 2 weeks prepartum. Such behaviour leads to confusion over lamb ownership and sometimes to later rejection of the ewe's own lamb when it is born.

2. Fostering. Some ewes, should they lose their own lambs, by death or other means, will make vigorous attempts to adopt alien lambs. Again, disputed ownership of a lamb does not enhance its prospects of survival.

3. Delayed grooming postpartum. Some ewes fail to groom their lambs at birth. A great many of those which give birth to twins or triplets fail to show satisfactory grooming towards the second or third born lamb. Ungroomed lambs remain wet and, in a cold environment, are more prone to suffer adversely from hypothermia.

4. Maternal desertion. Ewes, particularly young ones, sometimes desert their newborn lambs immediately following the birth. Deserted lambs usually die quickly if they have not been able to obtain any milk.

5. Butting of lambs. Aside from straightforward desertion, there may be a form of maternal–neonate disharmony in the form of aggressive behaviour directed by an ewe towards its lamb. The

ewe, butting the newborn lamb away from her, very quickly discourages the teat-seeking chain of behavioural actions so necessary for the lamb's early learning of feeding behaviour.

6. Refusal to stand and facilitate teat suckling. Ewes of any age group may show this form of anomalous behaviour. The ewe typically edges away from the lamb when the latter is teat-seeking. For teat-seeking activities to take place successfully the mother has to remain stationary. In this condition teat-seeking or et-epimeletic behaviour becomes exhausted in time.

It can be seen that many anomalies in behaviour can result in animals being impaired in terms of production. Certainly anomalous reproductive behaviour constitutes a major obstacle to optimum reproductive output; and for this reason, if for no other, behavioural problems must be recognized more clearly. Oestrus and libido are important prerequisites for breeding and it is in these areas that some of the most important examples of anomalous behaviour occur.

The recognition of anomalous behaviour is of growing importance. There is an ever-increasing realization that abnormalities in behaviour are early-warning signs of an animal's environmental circumstances being unsatisfactory. By pinpointing deficient environments in this way it may be possible to prevent stressors being applied to farm animals to an ever-increasing extent. With the development of applied ethology it is hoped that stress may be prevented from becoming the principal disease complex of animals under modern conditions of husbandry.

# SUPPLEMENTARY READING

CALHOUN, J. B. (1962) A behavioral sink. In: *Roots of Behavior*, ed. E. L. Bliss, pp. 295–315. New York: Harper Bros.

FOX, M. W. (1968) *Abnormal Behavior in Animals*. London: Saunders.

FRASER, A. F. (1963) Behavior disorders in domestic animals. *Cornell Vet.*, *53*, 213–223.

FRASER, A. F. (1968) Anomalies in reproductive behavior in farm animals. In: *Abnormal Behavior in Animals*, ed. M. W. Fox, chapter 14. London: Saunders.

# Glossary

*Aggressive Behaviour*: The tendency to initiate a vigorous conflict.

*Agonistic Behaviour*: Any behaviour associated with conflict or fighting between two individuals. It includes patterns of behaviour involving escape or passivity.

*Allelomimetic Behaviour*: Any behaviour where animals perform the same activity with some degree of mutual stimulation and consequent co-ordination.

*Competition*: (1) The direct struggle between individuals for a limited supply of environmental necessities. (2) The common striving for living requirements such as food, space or shelter, by two or more individuals, populations or species.

*Conditioning*: (1) This occurs when a reflex is modified by specific experience. (2) It occurs in a conditioned reflex when the original stimulus has been substituted. (3) The process by which an animal acquires the capacity to respond to a given stimulus with the reflex reaction proper to another stimulus (the re-inforcement) when the two stimuli are applied concurrently a number of times.

*Consummatory Act*: An act which constitutes the termination of a given instinctive behaviour pattern.

*Contactual Behaviour*: Maintenance of bodily contact. The formation of simple aggregations through behaviour of this sort occurs very commonly in animals.

*Critical Period*: The infantile phase when the subject is most sensitive to specific environmental features and experiences.

*Displacement Activity*: (1) An activity belonging to an instinct other than the one activated. (2) An activity performed by an animal in which two or more compatible drives are strongly activated. (3) Activities performed by an animal in which one drive is, at the same time, both activated and thwarted. (4) The performance of a behaviour pattern out of the context of behaviour to which it is normally related.

*Dominance*: (1) An individual animal is said to be dominant over another when it has priority in feeding and sexual behaviour, and when it is superior in aggressiveness and in group control. (2) Dominance status is indicated by superiority in fighting ability of one individual over one or more species mates. (3) A dominant animal is

185

one the behaviour of which proceeds without reference to the behaviour patterns of a subordinate animal.

*Drive*: The complex of internal and external states and stimuli leading to a given behaviour pattern.

*Eliminative Behaviour*: Patterns of behaviour connected with elimination of faeces and urine.

*Epimeletic Behaviour*: The provision in behavioural terms of care or attention; includes suckling in particular.

*Et-epimeletic Behaviour*: Care-seeking behaviour in the young animal; includes soliciting maternal attendance in particular.

*Ethogram*: An inventory of behaviour patterns typical of an animal or species.

*Flight Reaction*: A characteristic escape reaction, specific for a particular enemy and surroundings, occurring as soon as the intruder approaches.

*Flight Distance*: That radius of surrounding area within which intrusion provokes a flight reaction.

*Habituation*: The permanent weakening of a response as a result of repeated stimulation unaccompanied by re-inforcement. This is regarded as distinct from fatigue.

*Hierarchy*: Any social rank or order established through direct combat, threat, passive submission or some combination of these behaviour patterns.

*Home Range*: That locality where the individual animal imprints its principal functions.

*Imprinting*: (1) A rapid and usually very stable form of learning taking place in early life. (2) The infantile parameter whereby, often without any apparent immediate re-inforcement, broad supra-individual characteristics of the species come to be recognized as the species pattern and subsequently used as releasers.

*Ingestive Behaviour*: Behaviour concerned with the selection and consumption of food and drink.

*Innate Releasing Mechanism*: A hypothetical mechanism which is to prevent all discharge of activity unless the animal encounters the right environmental situation to release this block.

*Instinct*: (1) An inherited and adapted system of co-ordination within the nervous system as a whole which, when activated, finds expression in behaviour culminating in a fixed pattern. (2) A general term applied to behaviour differences which are largely determined by heredity.

*Kinesis*: An undirected reaction, without orientation of the body in relation to the stimulus.

*Leadership*: A special form of facilitation, in which one animal sets the pace of group activity or initiates changes in it.

*Learning*: The process which produces adaptive change in individual behaviour as the result of experience. It is regarded as distinct from fatigue, sensory adaptation, maturation and the consequences of bodily changes of any kind.

*Libido*: Used synonymously with male sex drive in domesticated animals.

*Overflow Activities*: Reactions to meagre or abnormal stimuli.

*Peck Dominance*: The dominance of one individual over others in most of their contacts.

*Peck Order*: (1) The rank of several members within a social hierarchy. (2) Arrangements according to dominance.

*Pheromone*: (1) A substance secreted by one individual and received by a second individual of the same species, releasing a specific reaction of behaviour or a developmental process. (2) Ectohormone.

*Reaction Time*: Time between application of stimulus and response of whole animal.

*Reflex*: An innate and simple response involving the central nervous system and occurring very shortly after the stimulus which evokes it. It characteristically involves only a part of the organism, though the whole may be affected, and is usually a response to localized stimuli.

*Releasers*: Characters which are peculiar to individuals of a given species and to which responsive releasing mechanisms of other individuals react, thus setting in motion chains of instinctive actions.

*Ritual Behaviour*: (1) Behaviour which has lost its original meaning and acquired a new one as a means of expression. (2) An originally variable sequence of behavioural actions which has become an unchangeable ceremony.

*Social Behaviour*: (1) The reciprocal interactions of two or more animals and the resulting modifications of individual action systems. (2) Any behaviour caused by or affecting another animal, usually one of the same species.

*Social Organization*: An aggregation of individuals into a fairly well-integrated and self-consistent group in which the unity is based upon the interdependence of the separate organisms.

*Social Releaser*: Any specific or complex feature of an organism eliciting an instinctive activity in another individual of the same or another species.

*Stimulus, Primary or Releaser*: Specific stimulus to which certain responses are automatically given. Such responses form the basis of learning, in early development.

*Taxis*: (1) Locomotion either directly towards or away from a source of stimulation. (2) Locomotory behaviour involving a steering reaction. (3) The spatial correction movement resulting in orientation.

*Territoriality*: Proprietary behaviour in respect of defence of all or part of the home range of an animal. This defence is directed primarily against members of the same species.

*Tonic Immobility*: (1) A state of locomotor economy, shown particularly in an unwillingness to make responses which involve complex, co-ordinated bodily movements. (2) An apparent absence of co-ordinated responses in an animal without an associated physical impairment.

# Index

Bull(s)—*cont.*
  low sex drive in   178
  psychic impotence of   178–9
  remating   121
  sexual behaviour patterns   105–7, 109
  somnolent behaviour   180
Butting in breeding goats   105

Calcium, necessity of   172
Calf (calves)
  birth   141–2
  controlling   91–2, 95
  grazing and feeding   50, 51
  grooming   157
  handling of   90, 91
  nursing   157
  suckling   150
Cannibalism   144, 176, 181
Care-giving behaviour   13
Care-seeking behaviour   13
Cattle (*see also* Bull; Calf; Cow)
  adrenal virilism   171
  behaviour patterns   50–62
    agonistic   55–7
    elimination   54–5
    exploration   60
    grooming   61–2
    ingestion   50–4
    play activites   50–60
    sleeping and resting   60–1
  social patterns   55–60
  biostimulation   116–17
  climatic influences   78–82
  control of   89–92
  courtship   110
  cystic ovarian disease in   171–2
  defaecation   134
  drinking   80
  fetus   130–3
  foot pains of   168
  hypocalcaemia in   170
  infections of   85
  lameness in   170
  milk fever   172–4
  neonatal behaviour   150
  oestrus
    post-parturient   114
    signs of   111, 113, 180
  pains in   169
  sexual behaviour   109
  social interaction of   157
  tending-bond formation   125
  thermoregulation   78–9

Cattle—*cont.*
  transport of   84–5
  wing shoulder in   168
Central nervous system   28
Cerebral
  cortex   29–30, 31
    sensory areas   29
    cortical necrosis   170
Cerebrum   4
  hormones and   31
Cervical vertebrae, lesion in   167
Challenges   106
Chant de coeur   26
Cheviot sheep   63, 82
Chronic laminitis   167
Clinical disorders, behaviour and   163–74
Colic   169
Columbia sheep   63
Coma in milk fever   172, 173
Community feeding of pigs   71
Competition   185
Complex hierarchy   58
Concept of
  drive   19–20, 164
  instinct   14–16
  motivation   164
  stimulation   164
  stress   20–21
Conditioning responses   18, 19, 185
Consummatory act   185
Contactual behaviour   185
Controlling animals   88–92
Coprophagia   177
Corriedale sheep   82
Courtship behaviour   106–9, 125–6
Cow(s)
  parturient behaviour   141–2, 146
  placentophagia in   138
  pre-parturient behaviour   136
  restraint of hind limb movement   95
  silent heat in   180
  udder-kinch for   94
Crib-biting   11, 176
Critical period   185
Crushes   88–9
Cystic ovarian disease, cattle   171–2

Daily cycle of behaviour, sheep   63–4
Dairy
  cattle, eating   52
  herds, dominance in   57–8
Dams and auditory stimulation   27

# Index